Vocabulary
in Context

FOR THE COMMON CORE STANDARDS

Grade
4

Table of Contents

Introduction

Steck-Vaughn's *Vocabulary in Context* series offers parents and educators high-quality, curriculum-based products that align with the Common Core Standards for English Language Arts for grades 2–9.

Each unit in the *Vocabulary in Context* books includes:

• fiction and/or nonfiction selections, covering a wide variety of topics

• context activities, ascertaining that students understand what they have read

• vocabulary activities, challenging students to show their understanding of key vocabulary

• questions in a standardized-test format, helping prepare students for standardized exams

• word skills activities, targeting additional vocabulary words and vocabulary skills

• writing activities, providing assignments that encourage students to use the vocabulary words

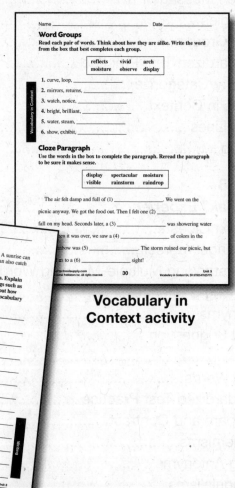

Reading selection

Vocabulary in Context activity

Word Skills activity

Writing activity

Homophones

Homophones are words that sound the same but have different meanings and usually have different spellings.

ant—aunt	groan—grown	right—write
ate—eight	heal—heel	road—rode—rowed
base—bass	here—hear	sail—sale
be—bee	hi—high	sea—see
beach—beech	hoarse—horse	seen—scene
bear—bare	hole—whole	sew—so—sow
beat—beet	hour—our	sight—cite—site
berry—bury	I—eye	some—sum
blew—blue	made—maid	son—sun
bored—board	meat—meet	sore—soar
bow—bough	new—knew	stair—stare
brake—break	no—know	steal—steel
buy—by	oar—or	their—there—they're
cell—sell	one—won	through—threw
cent—sent—scent	pail—pale	to—too—two
close—clothes	pain—pane	wail—whale
dear—deer	pair—pear	weak—week
flew—flu	peace—piece	we'll—wheel
flour—flower	peek—peak	wait—weight
for—four	plane—plain	way—weigh
forth—fourth	principal—principle	wood—would

Homographs

Homographs are words that are spelled the same but have different meanings and different origins (*bat*—the mammal, *bat*—the club). Some homographs also have different pronunciations (*august*—majestic, *August*—eighth month).

close < shut / near

dove < pigeon / did dive

live < to exist / having life

desert < abandon / arid land

object < thing / disagree

record < to make note of / best achievement

tear < rip / drop of water from an eye

refuse < to say no / trash

lead < heavy metal / to be first

does < form of *do* / female deer

Prefixes

Prefixes are letter groups added before a base word to change or add to the word's meaning.

Prefix	Meaning	Example
auto-	self	autobiography
bi-	two	bicycle, biweekly
dis-	not	disbelief
im-	not	impossible
in-	into, not	inside, independence
non-	not	nonfiction
pre-	before	prehistoric
re-	again	resend
tele-	far	telescope
trans-	across	transportation
tri-	three	triangle
uni-	one	unify

Vocabulary in Context G4, SV 9780547625775

Suffixes

Suffixes are letter groups added after a base word to change or add to the word's meaning.

Suffix	Meaning	Example
-er	one who	teacher
-er	more	brighter
-est	most	brightest
-ful	full of	wonderful
-ing	(present tense)	smiling
-less	without	penniless
-ling	small	duckling
-ly	every	weekly
-ly	(adverb)	quickly
-ness	state of being	happiness
-or	one who	actor
-y	state of	funny

Vocabulary in Context G4, SV 9780547625775

Lights! Lasers! Action!

Read the passage. Think about the meanings of the boldfaced words. Then go back to the passage. Underline the words or sentences that give you a clue to the meaning of each boldfaced word.

Brightly colored beams of light fly through the air. Some of them form shapes such as circles and triangle. Others form more lifelike images. They make **realistic** pictures of people and animals. Welcome to a laser light show!

Lasers are tools that **produce** very powerful beams of light. The light that a laser makes is so strong that it can cut a diamond. What makes laser light so powerful? It is very narrow, so it doesn't spread out as it travels. Doctors use lasers. For example, a **physician** can use the beam to cut like a knife. Businesses use them to power machines. In light shows, lasers also have an **artistic** use. They are used to create beauty.

The first laser light show took place in 1973 in the United States. Since then, people have been held **spellbound** by the colors and patterns in these displays. They find it difficult to take their eyes away from the magical beams. In today's laser light shows, the people who control the lasers often **focus** the beams on a wall. Aiming the beam at the wall **transforms** it into a movie screen for laser light pictures. Sometimes the laser **operators** direct the light at mirrors placed around the area. Each mirror reflects the beam onto another mirror for a dazzling effect.

Laser light shows can be found at many theme parks, plays, and sporting events. People around the world **marvel** at the exciting displays. They are filled with wonder as a dark sky suddenly comes alive with dancing lights. Laser light shows **impress** everyone who watches them. They leave people amazed by their magic.

8

Name _____ Date _____

Context Clues

Read each sentence. Look for clues to help you complete each sentence with a word from the box. Write the word on the line.

physician	focus	operators	artistic	spellbound
transforms	realistic	produce	marvel	impress

1. Lasers are machines that _____ very strong beams of light.

2. A _____ can use a laser beam to cut like a knife.

3. The people who create laser light shows use their _____ talents to create beautiful pictures.

4. In a laser light show, laser beams can be used to create very _____ pictures of people.

5. The people who create shows with laser lights can _____ the beams on walls and mirrors.

6. Laser light directed at a wall _____, or changes, the wall into a movie screen.

7. Many people _____ at the light and color created by laser beams.

8. Some people are so _____ by laser light shows that they stare at the designs for a long time.

9. The job of laser _____ is to control the beams.

10. The magical light and color of a laser light show are sure to _____ anyone!

Rewriting Sentences

Rewrite each sentence using one of the words from the box.

produce	physician	transforms

1. You should see a doctor about that cut on your knee.

_____

2. In a fairy tale, the kiss from a princess changes a frog into a prince.

_____

3. Our town has a factory that uses iron to make steel.

_____

Understanding Multiple-Meaning Words

The words in the box have more than one meaning. Look for clues in each sentence to tell which meaning is being used. Write the letter of the meaning next to the correct sentence.

impress	produce	focus
a. make a mark on	**a.** fresh fruit and vegetables	**a.** concentrate
b. amaze	**b.** to bring forth	**b.** aim light beams

_____ **1.** We can impress the wax because it is soft.

_____ **2.** A great movie will impress many people.

_____ **3.** A hamster can produce babies every eight weeks.

_____ **4.** We bought produce and meat at the farmer's market.

_____ **5.** Tonight I need to focus on finishing my book.

_____ **6.** You can use a magnifying glass to focus sunlight.

Analogies

An **analogy** shows how two words go together in the same way as two other words. A kitten is a baby cat and a puppy is a baby dog. So you could say: *Kitten* is to *cat* as *puppy* is to *dog*.

Write the words from the box to complete the following analogies.

impress   marvel   artistic   produce

1. *Know* is to *understand* as _____ is to *wonder*.

2. *Whisper* is to *yell* as _____ is to *destroy*.

3. *Musical* is to *music* as _____ is to *artist*.

4. *Scare* is to *frighten* as _____ is to *amaze*.

Dictionary Skills

Write the words from the box in alphabetical order, one word on each line. Then turn to the Glossary, beginning on page 108. Find each word in the Glossary. Write its meaning below.

physician   spellbound   focus   transforms
operators   realistic   artistic   impress

1. _____

2. _____

3. _____

4. _____

5. _____

6. _____

7. _____

8. _____

Vocabulary in Context

Idea Completion

Complete the following sentences.

1. In an artist's hands, clay *transforms* into _____
_____ .

2. Most people *marvel* at the Grand Canyon because _____
_____ .

3. A person might visit a *physician* when _____
_____ .

4. You can show your *artistic* side by _____
_____ .

5. It is important for a flashlight to have good *focus* because _____
_____ .

6. I sat *spellbound* when _____
_____ .

7. A *realistic* painting can be described as _____
_____ .

8. From paper, scissors, and paint, I could *produce* _____
_____ .

9. Bulldozer *operators* most likely had training in _____
_____ .

10. I *impress* others when I _____
_____ .

12

Vocabulary in Context

Name _____ Date _____

Standardized Test Practice

Read the sentences. Pick the word that best completes the second sentence. Circle the letter for the correct word.

> **TIP**
> Read the first sentence carefully. It will help you choose the missing word in the second sentence.

(sidebar) Vocabulary in Context

1. My uncle wants to practice medicine. He plans to be a _____.
   A physician   C coach
   B lawyer   D child

2. Sara drew a lifelike picture of her mother. It looked very _____.
   A green   C messy
   B realistic   D tired

3. There is an auto factory. It can _____ many cars each day.
   A laugh   C produce
   B drive   D grow

4. Those people control the machines. They are the _____.
   A persons   C doctors
   B actors   D operators

5. I can't find my way in the dark. Please _____ the flashlight over here.
   A focus   C remove
   B break   D finish

6. The campers are surprised to see so many stars. They _____ at the sight.
   A stop   C marvel
   B match   D sleep

7. The boy drew and painted all the posters for the show. He has a lot of _____ talent.
   A weak   C mechanical
   B artistic   D awful

8. That movie is the best one I have ever seen. It will really _____ you.
   A sadden   C impress
   B annoy   D bore

9. The new coat of paint makes a big change. It _____ this room.
   A chooses   C builds
   B cleans   D transforms

10. I could hardly move when I heard the music. I was _____ by the melody.
    A wakened   C spellbound
    B framed   D lost

Name _____ Date _____

Suffixes

When added to a noun or verb, the suffixes –*eer*, –*er*, and –*or* often stand for "one who." Complete the following sentences with a word from the box. Then write a definition for the word. The first one has been done for you.

| auctioneer | mountaineer | volunteer | jeweler |
| pioneer | engineer | senator | photographer |

1. The ____photographer____ used a camera with a powerful lens to take pictures of the lions.

   one who takes photographs
   _____

2. Long ago, trains used steam engines that were powered by coal. The train driver was called an _____.

   _____

3. The _____ called for higher bids on the antique furniture.

   _____

4. As an experienced _____, Joel planned to climb Mount McKinley.

   _____

5. The voters re-elected the _____ to office because of the work he had done for his state.

   _____

6. Ms. Acosta had her broken earring repaired by the _____.

   _____

Unit 1
Vocabulary in Context G4, SV 9780547625775

Word Skills

Multiple-Meaning Words

Read each sentence below. Then circle the letter next to the correct meaning of each underlined word.

1. My neighbor is a <u>volunteer</u> at the hospital.

   A a person who works without pay

   B to give or offer readily

2. The inventor hopes to <u>engineer</u> a new type of electric motor.

   A a person who maintains machines

   B to create and make plans for something

3. Thomas Edison <u>pioneered</u> recording and playing back on a phonograph.

   A to be the first to do something

   B a person who explores an area before anyone else

4. The fire <u>chief</u> gives orders to the firefighters.

   A the leader of a group

   B most important, main

5. The team of <u>mountaineers</u> planned a two-week hike in the Himalayas.

   A people who live on a mountain

   B people who climb mountains for enjoyment

6. My puppy likes to sit in my <u>lap</u>.

   A the front part of the body between the waist and the knees of a seated person

   B one time around or over the entire length of something

7. Brad found an injured sparrow and will <u>nurse</u> it back to health.

   A a person who takes care of the sick

   B to take care of someone or something that is ill

8. I am learning how to <u>iron</u> my own shirts.

   A to press clothes to remove wrinkles

   B a hard metal

Word Skills

Name _____   Date _____

Using Dictionary Skills

For each word below, circle the letter of the pair of guide words that could be at the top of a dictionary page containing the word.

1. volunteer
   A vision/vocabulary
   B vitamin/volcano
   C voile/votary
   D visitor/voice

2. photographer
   A phonics/phrase
   B pharmacy/photocopy
   C photography/piano
   D photon/physics

3. senator
   A school/semester
   B season/senate
   C section/separate
   D saddle/select

4. jeweler
   A jellyfish/jewelry
   B jersey/jewel
   C jigsaw/juggle
   D justice/kale

5. auctioneer
   A attack/auction
   B aunt/awake
   C audible/awful
   D auburn/avenue

6. engineer
   A endanger/engine
   B endless/English
   C elevation/enchant
   D enough/entertain

Now write the guide words you might find on the page that contains these words.

7. horseshoe _____

8. wizard _____

9. pioneer _____

10. mountaineer _____

Word Skills

Writing

Suppose that you can create your own laser light show. You can decide where to have it. You can also choose the colors and shapes to use and the pictures to show. You can tell a story. You can make the lights change quickly or slowly.

On the lines below, tell about your laser light show. Use some vocabulary words from this unit in your writing.

_____

_____

_____

_____

_____

_____

_____

_____

_____

_____

_____

_____

Writing

An Island Is Born

Read the passage. Think about the meanings of the boldfaced words. Then go back to the passage. Underline the words or sentences that give you a clue to the meaning of each boldfaced word.

Before 1963, there was no Surtsey Island. Then one day, Surtsey came right out of the ocean! Many islands are formed in this way as volcanoes grow on the ocean floor.

What is a volcano? And how does one form an island? It starts deep inside Earth. There, the heat is so great that, like a giant **furnace**, it melts rock. This **molten** rock joins with gases and rises up under the ground. If the push upward is great enough, it can make an opening in Earth's surface. Because so much of Earth is covered by oceans, many of these openings appear under the water.

When a volcano **erupts**, the melted rock is thrown up into the water. This **lava** drops back to the ocean floor. There it cools into rock again. And slowly it builds a mountain. As more melted rock is thrown out, it flows down the sides of the mountain. Hard rock is formed on these **slopes**, building up land that grows higher as it spreads wider. Finally, after what may take many years, the mountain reaches the water's surface. It seems to appear suddenly as a tiny island. Still the hot rock **overflows** onto the top of the mountain, adding more land above the water.

In time, the island may grow large enough for many people to settle on it. The Hawaiian Islands were formed this way. The volcano that formed an island may remain **active**, spitting fire and melted rock. In that case, the people must learn to live with this danger. They learn the signs, or **warnings**, that tell when the volcano will erupt. When they feel rumblings in the earth, the people **flee**. They run to find **refuge** on a safer part of the island. There they must wait until the volcano is quiet again.

Name _____ Date _____

Context Clues

Meanings for the vocabulary words are given below. Go back to the passage and read each sentence that has a vocabulary word. If you still cannot tell the meaning, look for clues in the sentences that come before and after the one with the vocabulary word. Write each word from the box in front of its meaning.

molten	refuge	active	overflows	furnace
lava	slopes	warnings	erupts	flee

1. _____ : melted rock from a volcano

2. _____ : signals or signs that tell of danger

3. _____ : a closed-in space in which heat is produced

4. _____ : melted by heat

5. _____ : to run away from danger

6. _____ : working; showing action

7. _____ : sides of hills or mountains

8. _____ : a place that provides protection

9. _____ : runs over the top or brim

10. _____ : bursts out; releases suddenly

Challenge Yourself

1. Name two warnings you might hear on a weather report.

_____

2. Volcanoes are active, but so are you. Name two active things you do.

_____

Vocabulary in Context G4, SV 9780547625775

Vocabulary in Context

Synonyms

Remember that synonyms are words that have the same or almost the same meaning. Match the words in the box with their synonyms listed below. Write each word on the line.

overflows	refuge	erupts	warnings

1. cautions _____

2. floods _____

3. explodes _____

4. shelter _____

Dictionary Skills

Guide words are the two words at the top of each page. They show the first and last entries on that page. All the words in between are in alphabetical order.

Look at the pairs of guide words. On the lines below each pair, write the words from the box that would appear on the same dictionary page. Be sure to put them in alphabetical order.

slopes	active	lava
furnace	flee	molten

ability/game

1. _____

2. _____

3. _____

lady/sudden

4. _____

5. _____

6. _____

Vocabulary in Context

Name _____ Date _____

Crossword Puzzle

Use the clues and the words in the box to complete the crossword puzzle.

erupts	warnings	flee	furnace	active
refuge	molten	lava	slopes	overflows

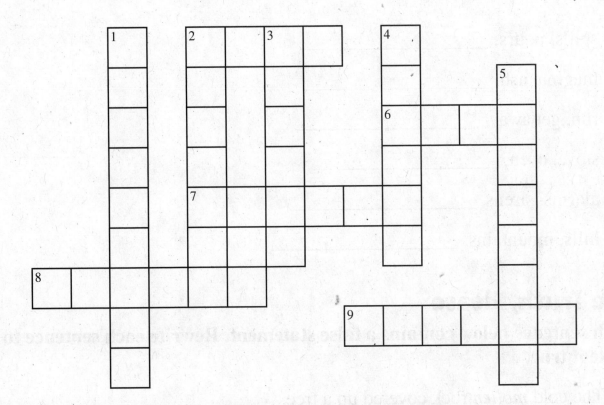

Across

2. to run away
6. melted rock
7. on the go
8. hillsides
9. safe place

Down

1. spills over
2. a very hot place
3. blows up
4. melted by heat
5. danger signals

Name _____ Date _____

Word Groups

Read each pair of words. Think about how they are alike. Write the word from the box that best completes each group.

slopes	furnace	flee
lava	overflows	warnings

1. spills, pours, _____

2. magma, ash, _____

3. run, get away, _____

4. stove, oven, _____

5. alarms, sirens, _____

6. hills, mountains, _____

The Truth, Please

Each sentence below contains a false statement. Rewrite each sentence to make it true.

1. The cold *molten* rock covered up a tree.

_____

2. As a volcano *erupts*, the mountain becomes quiet and still.

_____

3. A good place to take *refuge* from a tornado is a busy highway.

_____

4. It is smart to build a city near the top of an *active* volcano.

_____

Vocabulary in Context

Standardized Test Practice

Read each phrase. Look for the word or words that have the same or almost the same meaning as the boldfaced word. Circle the letter for the correct word.

> **TIP**
> Think about the meaning of the boldfaced word before you choose an answer. Don't be fooled by a word that looks like the boldfaced word.

1. **active** player
   A actual   C sleeping
   B working   D huge

2. sudden **warnings**
   A tears   C songs
   B warriors   D signals

3. seeks **refuge**
   A repair   C gifts
   B shelter   D people

4. **molten** rock
   A magic   C black
   B cooled   D melted

5. metal **furnace**
   A heating space
   B cooling space
   C watering place
   D furniture

6. hot **lava**
   A dirt   C melted rock
   B lace   D small rocks

7. volcano **erupts**
   A explodes   C quiets
   B hardens   D escapes

8. **flee** danger
   A go toward   C weed out
   B run from   D fight

9. mountain **slopes**
   A spirits   C goats
   B insects   D sides

10. lake **overflows**
    A floods   C heats
    B colors   D outruns

Name _____ Date _____

Classify/Categorize

Read the words in each group below. Name the category to which each group belongs. Then add another word to the list. The first one has been done for you.

1. **A** sediment
   B deposits
   C rivers
   Category: _words related to_
   rock formation
   Add: _sand_

2. **A** magma
   B volcanic
   C seismograph
   Category: _____
   _____
   Add: _____

3. **A** geologist
   B photographer
   C geographer
   Category: _____
   _____
   Add: _____

4. **A** gravity
   B planets
   C rotation
   Category: _____
   _____
   Add: _____

5. **A** petroleum
   B fossils
   C minerals
   Category: _____
   _____
   Add: _____

6. **A** geometry
   B geology
   C geode
   Category: _____
   _____
   Add: _____

7. **A** granite
   B quartz
   C topaz
   Category: _____
   _____
   Add: _____

8. **A** faults
   B tremors
   C plates
   Category: _____
   _____
   Add: _____

Word Skills

Vocabulary in Context G4, SV 9780547625775

Name _____ Date _____

Compare and Contrast

Complete the following sentences to describe how the two things named are alike or different. Use a dictionary to find the meanings of unknown words.

1. *Summer* is like *winter* because _____

_____.

2. *Petroleum* is like *gasoline* but _____

_____.

3. *Gravity* is like *glue* but _____

_____.

4. *Magma* is like *rock* except that _____

_____.

5. A *seismograph* is like a *speedometer* because _____

_____.

6. A *stalactite* is like *stalagmite* but _____

_____.

7. The *Rockies* are like the *Andes* except that _____

_____.

8. A *diamond* is like a *ruby* because _____

_____.

9. *Iron* is like *gold* but _____

_____.

10. A *gemologist* is like a *geologist* because _____

_____.

Unit 2
Vocabulary in Context G4, SV 9780547625775

Word Skills

Name _____ Date _____

Suffixes

Complete each sentence by adding a suffix to the word in parentheses.
Choose one of the suffixes from the box below. Write the new word in
the sentence.

Suffixes	Definition
-ed	an action or state in the past
-ic	related to, like
-ary	connected with, relating to
-er, -ist	a person who does something

1. A _____ is a person who studies the history of Earth.
   (geology)

2. Lava is _____ rock. (melt)

3. The firefighter's actions were _____. (hero)

4. The fire _____ all night. (burn)

5. The _____ ash fell many miles from the eruption. (volcano)

6. Limestone is _____ rock formed from small pieces of other
   rocks. (sediment)

7. A strong earthquake _____ the seaport. (destroy)

8. A _____ studies Earth and its inhabitants. (geography)

Vocabulary in Context G4, SV 9780547625775

Word Skills

Name _____ Date _____

Writing

Imagine that you are on vacation in Hawaii. You go to visit Mauna Loa, the biggest volcano. Just as you are about to take a photograph, the mountain rumbles. You escape to safety, but you are close enough to see the volcano erupt.

Write an article for the local newsletter telling about your adventure. Describe what you saw and heard when the volcano erupted. Use some vocabulary words from this unit in your writing.

_____

_____

_____

_____

_____

_____

_____

_____

_____

Vocabulary in Context G4, SV 9780547625775

Writing

Rainbows

Read the passage. Think about the meanings of the boldfaced words. Then go back to the passage. Underline the words or sentences that give you a clue to the meaning of each boldfaced word.

A rainbow is an **arch** of colors in the sky. This curved shape is formed when the sun shines after a **rainstorm**. You can see a rainbow only at certain times. To **observe** it, you need to have the sun behind you. The rain must be in front of you.

A rainbow is a **spectacular** sight. It makes people stare in wonder. A rainbow has six colors–violet, blue, green, yellow, orange, and red. These colors are also present in sunlight. But they are very **vivid** in a rainbow. They appear brighter than usual.

A rainbow forms because of what happens when light shines on water. The sun shines on a **raindrop**. The water **reflects** the light, or sends it back. The light is broken up into separate colors.

Of course, the sun shines on many raindrops at once. Each raindrop breaks the light into the same six colors. Together, millions of raindrops form a **display** of colors called a rainbow.

Most people have seen rainbows in the sky. But they can form in other places, too. A rainbow can form wherever light shines on **moisture**, or wetness. Rainbows sometimes form in small puddles on the ground. The puddles can be made of water. Sometimes a rainbow is **visible** in a puddle of oil. You can also see a rainbow in water that squirts out of a garden hose.

Next time you see a rainbow, look at the colors. Can you name them?

Context Clues

Meanings for the vocabulary words are given below. Go back to the passage and read each sentence that has a vocabulary word. If you still cannot tell the meaning, look for clues in the sentences that come before and after the one with the vocabulary word. Write each word from the box in front of its meaning.

spectacular	observe	moisture	visible	rainstorm
reflects	display	vivid	raindrop	arch

1. _____: able to be seen

2. _____: a storm with a lot of rain

3. _____: show

4. _____: a single drop of rain

5. _____: very bright

6. _____: striking; amazing

7. _____: a curved shape

8. _____: to watch

9. _____: sends back, as in heat, light, or a picture

10. _____: water in the air

Challenge Yourself

1. Name two things you observe on your way to school.

_____

2. Name two things that are vivid in color.

_____

Word Groups

Read each pair of words. Think about how they are alike. Write the word from the box that best completes each group.

reflects	vivid	arch
moisture	observe	display

1. curve, loop, _____

2. mirrors, returns, _____

3. watch, notice, _____

4. bright, brilliant, _____

5. water, steam, _____

6. show, exhibit, _____

Vocabulary in Context

Cloze Paragraph

Use the words in the box to complete the paragraph. Reread the paragraph to be sure it makes sense.

display	spectacular	moisture
visible	rainstorm	raindrop

The air felt damp and full of (1) _____. We went on the

picnic anyway. We got the food out. Then I felt one (2) _____

fall on my head. Seconds later, a (3) _____ was showering water

on us. When it was over, we saw a (4) _____ of colors in the

sky. A rainbow was (5) _____. The storm ruined our picnic, but

it treated us to a (6) _____ sight!

Compound Words

A compound word is made up of two or more words. For example, *sail* and *boat* make up the compound word *sailboat*.

Join the word *rain* to each word to make four compound words. Write the new words.

                                    rain

bow   **1.** _____

drop   **2.** _____

storm   **3.** _____

coat   **4.** _____

Analogies

Remember that an analogy shows how two words go together in the same way as two other words. Write the words from the box to complete the following analogies.

reflects	vivid	arch	moisture
spectacular	display	observe	visible

1. *Cylinder* is to *soup can* as _____ is to *rainbow*.

2. *Frying pan* is to *cooks* as *mirror* is to _____.

3. *Make* is to *produce* as *show* is to _____.

4. *Unhappy* is to *happy* as *invisible* is to _____.

5. *Purchase* is to *buy* as *watch* is to _____.

6. *Glamorous* is to *movie star* as _____ is to *fireworks show*.

7. *Solid* is to *liquid* as *dryness* is to _____.

8. *Shiny* is to *new penny* as _____ is to *bright purple dress*.

Name _____ Date _____

Synonyms

Remember that synonyms are words that have the same or almost the same meaning. Cross out the word in each line that is not a synonym.

1. amazing   spectacular   wonderful   boring

2. see   inspect   ignore   observe

3. mistake   moisture   dampness   liquid

4. visible   hidden   noticeable   seen

5. arrangement   display   agreement   showing

6. bow   roof   arch   curve

Dictionary Skills

Write the words from the box in alphabetical order, one word on each line. Then turn to the Glossary, beginning on page 108. Find each word in the Glossary. Write its meaning below.

| vivid | rainstorm | reflects | raindrop | visible |

1. _____

2. _____

3. _____

4. _____

5. _____

Vocabulary in Context

Name _____ Date _____

Standardized Test Practice

Read each sentence. Pick the word that best completes the sentence. Circle the letter for the correct word.

TIP

If you are not sure which word completes the sentence, do the best you can. Try to choose the answer that makes the most sense.

Vocabulary in Context

1. When a **rainstorm** is reported, you know there are _____.
   - **A** snows
   - **B** droughts
   - **C** showers
   - **D** suns

2. A **spectacular** movie is one that you will _____.
   - **A** ignore
   - **B** build
   - **C** forget
   - **D** remember

3. A **vivid** painting has colors that are _____.
   - **A** boring
   - **B** bright
   - **C** bare
   - **D** big

4. When you **observe** something, you _____ it.
   - **A** touch
   - **B** break
   - **C** see
   - **D** smell

5. **Moisture** in a cellar will make it _____.
   - **A** dry
   - **B** damp
   - **C** dark
   - **D** glow

6. An **arch** is a _____.
   - **A** curve
   - **B** color
   - **C** flag
   - **D** name

7. A **visible** object is one that can be _____.
   - **A** heard
   - **B** tasted
   - **C** seen
   - **D** walked

8. If a **raindrop** lands on you, you become _____.
   - **A** visible
   - **B** sleepy
   - **C** happy
   - **D** wet

9. When an object **reflects** light, the light _____.
   - **A** melts
   - **B** disappears
   - **C** goes home
   - **D** comes back

10. A **display** of art could be a _____ of paintings.
    - **A** collection
    - **B** bucket
    - **C** house
    - **D** city

Name _____   Date _____

Explore Word Meanings

Write each of the words from the box under the categories below. Some words may fit in more than one category.

vapor	surroundings	climate	smog
ozone	atmosphere	ambiance	oxygen

1. Science words

_____

_____

_____

_____

3. Weather words

_____

_____

_____

_____

2. Describes the area around you

_____

_____

_____

4. Words with two syllables

_____

_____

_____

Now answer these questions. Think about the meaning of the underlined words.

5. Would you prefer to breathe <u>oxygen</u> or <u>smog</u>? Explain why.

_____

6. How is a restaurant's <u>ambiance</u> similar to its <u>surroundings</u>? How is it different?

_____

34

Word Skills

Multiple-Meaning Words

Determine the meaning of the underlined word as it is used in each sentence. Write the letter of the definition that matches each.

1. The smoke from vast forest fires added to the pollution of the <u>atmosphere</u>. _____

   There was an <u>atmosphere</u> of sportsmanship when the opposing teams met for the first time. _____

   A the layer of air surrounding Earth

   B the surrounding feeling of an environment

2. Citrus trees, such as the orange and tangerine, grow best in a tropical <u>climate</u>. _____

   The townspeople couldn't get enough of Yulee's Yummy Yogurt. The <u>climate</u> was right for Yulee to open a second store. _____

   A an atmosphere or feeling among people

   B a region having particular weather conditions

3. Isabella felt homesick at first, but she soon felt comfortable in her new <u>surroundings</u>. _____

   The trees <u>surrounding</u> the lake were tall and leafy, providing shade for campers. _____

   A enclosing on all sides

   B the conditions around you

4. Jerome auditioned for the lead part in the <u>musical</u>. _____

   Songbirds and crickets are among the <u>musical</u> animals that live in the woods. _____

   A a dramatic performance that includes singing

   B melodious, sounding like music

Name _____   Date _____

Classify/Categorize

In each of the following groups, three of the words are related in some way. Circle the letter of the one word that is not part of the group. Then name the category and add another word that fits.

1. **A** climate
   B conditions
   C environment
   D landforms

   Category: _____

   Add: _____

2. **A** oxygen
   B hydroplane
   C hydrogen
   D ozone

   Category: _____

   Add: _____

3. **A** vapor
   B sand
   C fumes
   D gases

   Category: _____

   Add: _____

4. **A** ambiance
   B mood
   C joyfulness
   D atmosphere

   Category: _____

   Add: _____

5. **A** atmosphere
   B spherical
   C sphinx
   D biosphere

   Category: _____

   Add: _____

6. **A** smog
   B haze
   C cloud
   D warmth

   Category: _____

   Add: _____

Word Skills

Vocabulary in Context G4, SV 9780547625775

Writing

A rainbow is not the only beautiful sight you can see in the sky. A sunrise can also be colorful, and so can a sunset. A full moon or a starry sky can also catch your attention.

Compare and contrast a rainbow to one of these other sky sights. Explain how they are alike and how they are different. Think about things such as how they look and what time of day you see them. Also think about how often you see them and how long they stay in the sky. Use some vocabulary words from this unit in your writing.

_____

_____

_____

_____

_____

_____

_____

_____

_____

_____

_____

_____

Writing

The King's Camel Race

Read the passage. Think about the meanings of the boldfaced words. Then go back to the passage. Underline the words or sentences that give you a clue to the meaning of each boldfaced word.

Picture 2,500 **camels** racing across the desert. Young Arab boys ride the humped animals, **coaxing** and urging them on. Dust clouds rise in the air. When one camel, then another, breaks out of the pack and **lunges** ahead, people cheer.

This **competition** is called the King's Camel Race. This twelve-mile event takes place every spring outside Riyadh, the capital of Saudi Arabia.

In this part of the world, camels are still very important. They are used for milk and meat and for travel in the desert. And sometimes they are raced like horses.

Because of the big prizes, many people want to win. So there are many **entries** in the race. Hundreds of other people come just to watch the **spectacle**. When the race is over, no one forgets the amazing sight.

Getting ready for the race takes work. The boys feed their camels a special mix of grains. They exercise them every day to prepare for the long race. But riding a camel is not easy. Even after weeks of practice, some boys still fall off their camels. Or they get tired of sitting on the beast and are forced to stop and **dismount**.

The top 200 riders all **qualify** for prizes from the king. But the best prizes go to the rider with the camel that **outruns** all the others. For this **champion**, the winner of the race, there is a gold dagger, money, and a truck.

Name _____ Date _____

Context Clues

Read each sentence. Look for clues to help you complete each sentence with a word from the box. Write the word on the line.

competition	spectacle	camels	qualify	coaxing
entries	dismount	champion	outruns	lunges

1. Humped animals called _____ are raced in the desert.

2. The Arab boys who enter the _____ are serious about winning the race.

3. To _____, or to be fit for the race, a boy needs a fast camel.

4. There are a great number of _____, or people in the contest, because the winner gets wonderful prizes.

5. The _____, or winner, of the camel race wins a truck!

6. The boy whose camel _____ all the others will win.

7. To urge his camel to run faster, a boy might talk to the beast,

   _____ it on.

8. A camel that obeys is the one that _____ forward in order to lead.

9. A camel may stop and force its rider to get down, or to

   _____, during the race.

10. A camel race in the desert is an amazing _____!

Base Words

Base words are words without any endings or other word parts added to them. For each word below, write its base word next to it on the line. Remember, sometimes the spelling of the base word changes when an ending is added to it.

1. camels _____

2. coaxing _____

3. dismounted _____

4. entries _____

5. lunges _____

Word Groups

Read each pair of words. Think about how they are alike. Write the word from the box that best completes each group.

spectacle	qualify	champion
competition	lunges	outruns

1. beats, tops, _____

2. contest, game, _____

3. winner, leader, _____

4. show, display, _____

5. pass, fit, _____

6. leaps, springs, _____

Name _____ Date _____

Word Puzzle

Write a word from the box next to each clue. Then write the words formed
by the letters in the squares. You will have the answer to the question below.

camel	lunges	entries	competition	outruns
coaxed	champion	spectacle	qualify	dismount

1. the winner __ __ __ ☐ __ __ __

2. those taking part in a contest __ __ __ __ ☐ __ __

3. to get off ☐ __ __ __ __ __ __

4. urged on __ __ __ __ __ ☐

5. moves forward suddenly ☐ __ __ __ __ __

6. contest __ __ __ __ ☐ __ __ __ __ __

7. a desert animal __ __ __ ☐ __

8. show to have the needed ability __ __ ☐ __ __ __ __

9. goes faster than others __ __ __ __ __ __ ☐ __

10. an amazing show __ __ __ __ ☐ __ __ __

To what part of the world would you go to see the King's Camel Race?

The _____ _____

Synonyms

Remember that synonyms are words that have the same or almost the same meaning. Cross out the word in each line that is not a synonym.

1. contest   competition   conflict   current

2. beat   outrun   sink   win

3. normal   show   spectacle   event

4. lunges   jumps   rests   pounces

5. fit   disqualified   prepared   qualified

6. worst   best   champion   chief

Rewriting Sentences

Rewrite each sentence using one of the words from the box.

camels	coaxing	dismount	entries

1. At the end of the race, riders stop and get off.

_____

2. Use gentle urging to get the mule to walk.

_____

3. I saw three animals with long necks and humps on their backs at the zoo.

_____

4. There are many people who are going to take part in the science fair.

_____

Vocabulary in Context

Name _____   Date _____

Standardized Test Practice

Read each sentence. Pick the word that best completes the sentence. Circle the letter for the correct word.

> **TIP**
> Some tests put letters before the answer choices. Be sure to find the letter of the answer you think is correct and then circle it.

1. All _____ have one or two humps.

   A rides   C elephants

   B camels   D champions

2. The rider decided to stop and _____.

   A dance   C dismount

   B approach   D preheat

3. She finished her work so she will _____ for a prize.

   A qualify   C overflow

   B dismount   D outrun

4. The camel _____ ahead and wins.

   A laughs   C lifts

   B listens   D lunges

5. Since there are twelve _____, there will be twelve runners in the race.

   A conflicts   C lavas

   B entries   D victors

6. A circus is a big _____.

   A crowd   C pioneer

   B spectacle   D person

7. The _____ will be held in the gym.

   A qualify   C warnings

   B city   D competition

8. Her medals prove that she is a _____ skater.

   A champion   C dirt

   B gravity   D icing

9. My horse _____ the others and wins the race.

   A overhears   C outruns

   B overflows   D outranks

10. The trainer is _____ the dog to roll over.

   A erupting   C refusing

   B outrunning   D coaxing

Analogies

Remember that an **analogy** is made of two pairs of words. The words in each pair are related in the same way.

Write a word to complete each of the following analogies.

1. *Competition* is to *competitor* as *sculpture* is to _____.

2. *Rival* is to *opponent* as *victor* is to _____.

3. *Tournament* is to *athletic* as *exhibition* is to _____.

4. *Disagreement* is to *conflict* as *competition* is to _____.

5. *Contender* is to *title* as *heir* is to _____.

6. *Finish line* is to *race* as _____ is to *book*.

7. *Lanes* are to *swimming pool* as _____ are to *notebook*.

8. *Entry form* is to *contest* as _____ is to *job*.

9. *Trophy* is to *prize* as _____ is to *vegetable*.

10. *Champion* is to *championship* as *sportsman* is to _____.

Word Skills

Word Families

Words can be related by a root or base word, or by word parts. In each group of words below, determine how the words are related. Then circle the letter of the word that is not related to the other three. The first one has been done for you.

1. **A** competition
   (**B**) compromise
   C compete
   D competitor
   Family: _____ *base word compete* _____

2. **A** contend
   B contender
   C contention
   D competition
   Family: _____

3. **A** opponent
   B opposition
   C oppose
   D opossum
   Family: _____

4. **A** rival
   B rivet
   C rivalry
   D rivalries
   Family: _____

5. **A** victory
   B victor
   C victorious
   D victim
   Family: _____

6. **A** torn
   B tourist
   C tournament
   D tourniquet
   Family: _____

7. **A** winning
   B sting
   C singing
   D racing
   Family: _____

8. **A** conflict
   B confusion
   C contract
   D counter
   Family: _____

Word Skills

Vocabulary in Context G4, SV 9780547625775

Name _____ Date _____

Classify/Categorize

Circle the letter of the word that does not belong in each group. Then name the category in the space provided.

1. A players
   B meet
   C tournament
   D contest

   Category: _____

2. A opponent
   B contestant
   C referee
   D contender

   Category: _____

3. A tennis
   B badminton
   C cycling
   D volleyball

   Category: _____

4. A infield
   B goal line
   C home plate
   D pitcher's mound

   Category: _____

5. A batting helmet
   B catcher's mask
   C chest guard
   D shoulder pads

   Category: _____

Unit 4
Vocabulary in Context G4, SV 9780547625775

Word Skills

Name _____ Date _____

Writing

The champion of the King's Camel Race wins a gold dagger, money, and a truck. Pretend that you are the winner of a bike race or a horse race. You have won a million dollars.

Use the lines below to write about what you would do with your prize money. Use some vocabulary words from this unit in your writing.

If I won one million dollars, I would _____

_____

_____

_____

_____

_____

_____

_____

_____

_____

_____

_____

Vocabulary in Context G4, SV 9780547625775

Writing

How Does Your Skin Grow?

Read the passage. Think about the meanings of the boldfaced words. Then go back to the passage. Underline the words or sentences that give you a clue to the meaning of each boldfaced word.

As you grow, your skin grows, too. In fact, throughout your **lifetime** your skin keeps growing. Stare at your arm for about 60 seconds. Can you see any change? Probably not. Now, with your fingernail, gently **scrape** the surface of your skin. What you see are tiny specks that are flakes of skin cells. This is quite **normal**. Every hour your body sheds about one million dead skin cells.

Skin is strong and tough. It protects the muscles and organs underneath. It also keeps dangerous germs from entering the body. What keeps your skin strong? Do you know how your skin grows?

Skin is made up of three layers. Each layer has a **function**, or a different job to do. The bottom layer is thick and holds sweat **glands** and **nerves**, which help you feel. The sweat glands **insulate**, or keep the body from getting too hot. Cells in the glands make sweat. Sweat reaches the surface of the skin and dries, keeping you cool.

The middle layer of your skin has millions of cells. These cells grow and divide into other cells. As new cells are made, some are pushed to the top layer. The cells pushed to the surface are dead skin cells. The dead layer of skin rubs off. Then a new layer of skin takes its place. This keeps your skin **healthy**. Your skin keeps growing this way even when you are a **mature** adult.

Imagine, every month you have an almost completely new outer skin! It would be truly amazing to watch this change happen. However, the growth and change of skin is **invisible** to the naked eye.

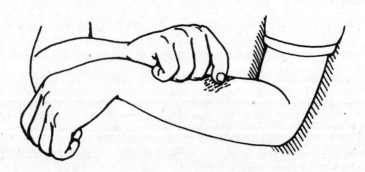

Context Clues

Meanings for the vocabulary words are given below. Go back to the passage and read each sentence that has a vocabulary word. If you still cannot tell the meaning, look for clues in the sentences that come before and after the one with the vocabulary word. Write each word from the box in front of its meaning.

lifetime	healthy	invisible	insulate	glands
mature	function	scrape	nerves	normal

1. _____: the length of a person's life

2. _____: to scratch the surface

3. _____: usual condition

4. _____: groups of cells that alert the body to feel heat, cold, and pain

5. _____: purpose

6. _____: organs that produce materials used by the body

7. _____: to protect something from getting too hot or too cold

8. _____: well; fit

9. _____: not able to be seen

10. _____: full-grown; developed

Challenge Yourself

1. Name two things that you can do to keep your skin healthy.

_____

2. Name two things that insulate your body from the cold.

_____

Synonyms

Synonyms are words that have the same or almost the same meaning.
Match the words from the box with their synonyms listed below. Write each
word on the line.

invisible	scrape	healthy
function	normal	mature

1. usual _____

2. job _____

3. unseen _____

4. fit _____

5. full-grown _____

6. scratch _____

Writing Sentences

Use each vocabulary word from the box to write an original sentence.

insulate	mature	nerves
lifetime	glands	healthy

1. _____

2. _____

3. _____

4. _____

5. _____

6. _____

Vocabulary in Context

Name _____ Date _____

Word Map

Use the vocabulary words in the box to complete the word map about the human body. Add other words that you know to each group. One heading will not have any vocabulary words, but only your words.

mature	normal	glands	healthy	nerves

Parts of the Body

1. _____
2. _____
3. _____
4. _____
5. _____

How a Body Can Look

1. _____
2. _____
3. _____
4. _____
5. _____

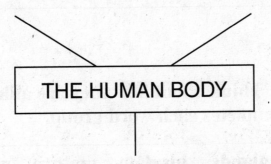

THE HUMAN BODY

What a Body Can Do

1. _____
2. _____
3. _____
4. _____
5. _____

Name _____ Date _____

Idea Completion

Complete each sentence below.

1. I would like to have a *lifetime's* supply of soap because _____
_____.

2. That baby looks *healthy* because _____
_____.

3. If I were *invisible* for one day, I would _____
_____.

4. There is a risk of getting a *scrape* if you _____
_____.

5. On a winter's day, my *nerves* tell me _____
_____.

Word Groups

Read each pair of words. Think about how they are alike. Write the word from the box that best completes each word group.

function	glands	insulate	mature	normal

1. average, regular, _____

2. adult, grown-up, _____

3. job, purpose, _____

4. protect, shield, _____

5. heart, lungs, _____

Name _____ Date _____

Standardized Test Practice

Read the phrase. Look for the word or words that have the same or almost the same meaning as the boldfaced word. Circle the letter for the correct word.

TIP
Think about the meaning of the boldfaced word before you choose an answer. Don't be fooled by a word that looks like the boldfaced word.

1. sweat **glands**
   A hairs   C organs
   B strands   D waters

2. **mature** adult
   A awake   C young
   B happy   D full-grown

3. important **function**
   A forecast   C day
   B purpose   D success

4. **invisible** gases
   A unseen   C interesting
   B fading   D valuable

5. **insulate** a house
   A search   C protect
   B look for   D inspire

6. **healthy** cat
   A helpless   C wealthy
   B sleepy   D well

7. long **lifetime**
   A dream   C lightning
   B length of life D end of life

8. **normal** day
   A usual   C northern
   B long   D important

9. **scrape** a knee
   A rest   C scold
   B bend   D scratch

10. **nerves** feel
   A nephews   C car parts
   B body parts   D plants

Multiple-Meaning Words

Read each sentence below. Then circle the letter next to the correct meaning of each underlined word.

1. Under my skin and muscles is my <u>skeleton</u>.

   A the main columns and beams, without walls

   B all the bones of a human body

2. The scientist's years of research laid the <u>framework</u> for his later inventions.

   A the beginning of a house before walls are added

   B a set of ideas from which to begin working

3. Do not eat the strawberries that have <u>mold</u> on them.

   A a type of fungus found on damp or decaying surfaces

   B a pan which gives food a decorative shape

4. I am using a microscope to study the <u>structure</u> of human cells.

   A what something is made of

   B a building

5. The teenager was of a small <u>frame</u> and easily slipped through the railings to save the stranded puppy.

   A an object used for displaying a photograph or painting

   B the physical make-up of the body

6. The gymnast used good <u>form</u> when she turned a somersault.

   A the way in which someone does something

   B a document with blank spaces to be filled with information

7. The <u>composition</u> of dark and light colors made the painting unusual.

   A a written essay

   B the way something is put together

8. In science we are using a skeleton to learn about human <u>anatomy</u>.

   A the way the parts are organized

   B the study of the parts of the body

Word Skills

Content-Area Words

Each numbered group contains special words for a certain topic or area of study. Write the topic or area from the box that fits the group.

drama   grammar   anatomy   social studies

1. skeleton, muscles, body composition _____

2. actors, stage, costumes, play _____

3. nations, states, capitals, governments _____

4. subject, sentence, verb, adverb _____

architecture   science   physical education   mathematics

5. subtraction, multiplication, algebra _____

6. football, basketball, fitness, form _____

7. framework, structure, base, foundation _____

8. mold, microscope, medicine, laboratory _____

Choose two topics or category labels from either of the boxes above. List at least three additional words related to each of the labels you chose.

9. Label: _____   **10.** Label: _____

_____   _____

_____   _____

_____   _____

Unit 5
Vocabulary in Context G4, SV 9780547625775

Word Skills

Name _____ Date _____

Compare and Contrast

Complete the following sentences to describe how the two things named are alike or different. Use a dictionary to find the meanings of unknown words.

1. *Frame* is like *skeleton* because _____

_____.

2. *Body composition* is like *anatomy* because _____

_____.

3. *Form* is like *function* except that _____

_____.

4. A *framework* is like an *outline* because _____

_____.

5. *Mold* is like *decay* because _____

_____.

6. *Structure* is like *anatomy* because _____

_____.

7. *Germs* are like *invisible things* except that _____

_____.

8. *Skeleton* is like *nerves* because _____

_____.

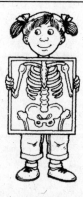

Word Skills

Writing

Your skin stays healthy by getting rid of dead cells. There are things that you can do, too, to help keep your skin in good health.

Look at the pictures. Use those ideas and others you have to write rules for taking care of your skin. Use some vocabulary words from this unit in your writing.

Rule 1: You should keep your skin healthy by _____

_____

_____

_____

_____

_____

_____

_____

_____

_____

Writing

The Great Space Race

Read the passage. Think about the meanings of the boldfaced words. Then go back to the passage. Underline the words or sentences that give you a clue to the meaning of each boldfaced word.

Some people believe the world's greatest race was the Space Race. The United States and the former Soviet Union raced to see which country would be the first to **conquer** outer space. When did the Space Race start? On October 4, 1957, the Soviet Union sent a **satellite** named *Sputnik I* into space. This tiny, human-made moon sent radio signals to people in **nations** around the world. The Space Age and the Space Race had begun!

The United States had hoped to **launch** a satellite first. But there was trouble at the U.S. rocket base when a rocket blew up. This caused a long **delay**. The United States did not send up its first satellite until January 31, 1958. So the Soviet Union took the early lead in the Space Race.

People around the globe watched to see which country would be first to send up a **spacecraft** with a person inside. On April 12, 1961, Yuri Gagarin, a Soviet **cosmonaut**, circled Earth. For the second time, the Soviet Union was **triumphant**. But the United States was very close behind. Just one month later, Alan Shepard became the first person from the United States in space.

Then the world wondered which country would be the first to land a rocket with people on board on the moon. The Soviet Union had been ahead. But scientists in the United States pushed hard to catch up. Finally, they jumped ahead. In December 1968, U.S. astronauts **orbited** the moon. Then in July of 1969, two others, Neil Armstrong and Edwin Aldrin, walked on the surface of the moon.

Later, both countries built space stations for gathering information. The countries started working together to collect **data** about outer space. Today, Russia and the United States work together to unlock the mysteries of the stars and more.

Name _____ Date _____

Context Clues

Read each sentence. Look for clues to help you complete each sentence with a word from the box. Write the word on the line.

spacecraft	conquer	orbited	cosmonaut	satellite
delay	nations	launch	triumphant	data

1. Two _____, the United States and the former Soviet Union, competed against each other in the Space Race.

2. They began the world's effort to _____, or win victory over, the unknown region of outer space.

3. Each country ran into more than one _____ that held up the path to victory.

4. The first step was to send a _____, a human-made moon, into space.

5. At first, it was the former Soviet Union that was _____, or successful.

6. Today many countries _____ satellites into space.

7. Some satellites send back _____, or information, about the weather.

8. Satellites have _____, or circled, Earth for many years.

9. It is an exciting event when a _____ with people inside is sent into outer space.

10. The former Soviet Union sent Valentina Tereshkova, the first woman _____, into space.

Vocabulary in Context G4, SV 9780547625775

Analogies

An analogy shows how two words go together in the same way as two other words. Write the words from the box to complete the following analogies.

delay	nation	satellite	spacecraft	cosmonaut

1. *Diver* is to *ocean* as _____ is to *space*.

2. *Rush* is to *go* as _____ is to *stop*.

3. *Car* is to *automobile* as _____ is to *moon*.

4. *Subway* is to *underground* as _____ is to *space*.

5. *City* is to *Dallas* as _____ is to *United States*.

Word Groups

Read each pair of words. Think about how they are alike. Write the word from the box that best completes each group.

nations	triumphant	orbit
data	launch	conquer

1. countries, governments, _____

2. send, begin, _____

3. circle, ring, _____

4. facts, information, _____

5. winning, successful, _____

6. defeat, win, _____

Rewriting Sentences

Rewrite each sentence using one of the words from the box.

data	delay	nations
orbited	spacecraft	triumphant

1. The rocket ship sat on the launch pad, waiting for the countdown to begin.

_____

2. There was a parade after the astronaut's successful return from space.

_____

3. The pilot had to put off until a later time our flight to Miami.

_____

4. I keep all that information stored on my laptop.

_____

5. The satellite traveled around Earth.

_____

6. Heads of state of different countries will meet in Toronto.

_____

The Truth, Please

Each sentence below contains a false statement. Rewrite each sentence to make it true.

1. Like the sun, a *satellite* sits still in the sky.

_____

2. If you *conquer* something, you give up and lose.

_____

Vocabulary in Context

Descriptions

Write the word from the box that fits the description.

nations   satellite   cosmonaut   launch   spacecraft

1. This long-nosed vehicle travels beyond Earth's gravity.

_____

2. These places have borders, their own governments, and people who share

a language. _____

3. This scientist from the former Soviet Union wears a spacesuit.

_____

4. This is what happens to a rocket after someone says, "5, 4, 3, 2, 1 . . . lift

off!" _____

5. This object orbits Earth like the moon does and is used to send information.

_____

Explore Word Meanings

Circle all the words that answer each question. Write a sentence using the underlined word and one of the circled words.

1. Who or what might <u>conquer</u>?

army   invader   plane   carpenter

_____

2. Who or what might be <u>delayed</u>?

football game   appointment   flight   watch

_____

Standardized Test Practice

Read each sentence. Pick the word that best completes the sentence. Circle the letter for the correct word.

TIP

If you are not sure which word completes the sentence, do the best you can. Try to choose the answer that makes the most sense.

1. To **launch** is to _____.
   A send off   C break down
   B clean up   D smash up

2. Something that has **orbited** Earth has _____ it.
   A broken   C circled
   B forgotten   D liked

3. A **triumphant** army has been _____.
   A defeated   C stolen
   B successful   D forgotten

4. A **spacecraft** is a _____.
   A dog   C spaceship
   B creature   D walk

5. The **nations** of the world are the different _____.
   A rivers   C mountains
   B countries   D continents

6. A **cosmonaut** is a _____.
   A star   C spaceship
   B moon   D space traveler

7. A **delay** is a _____.
   A birth   C deal
   B wait   D dress

8. If you collect **data**, you gather _____.
   A stamps   C information
   B money   D food

9. A **satellite** is a _____.
   A planet
   B sun
   C handmade lamp
   D human-made moon

10. When an army sets out to **conquer** a city, it wants to _____ it.
   A win   C find
   B lose   D build

Vocabulary in Context

Greek and Latin Roots

Many English words are borrowed from other languages. In Greek, for example, the root *astro* means "star" or "star-shaped."

Think about this information as you write answers for the following questions.

1. *Nautical* comes from the Greek word for *sailor*. What does *astronaut* mean?

   _____

2. The endings *-ics*, *-ogy*, and *-y* mean "the science or practice of." What does *astronautics* mean?

   _____

3. The suffix *-er* often means "a person who." What does an *astronomer* do?

   _____

4. If a *cuboid* is an object shaped something like a cube, what do you think an *asteroid* is?

   _____

5. If *nautical* means "having to do with the sea," what do you think *astral* means?

   _____

6. A dome is a rounded roof. What might an *astrodome* be used for?

   _____

7. An aster is a type of flower. Draw what you think it might look like.

Word Skills

Compare and Contrast

Complete the following sentences to describe how the two things named are alike or different. Use a dictionary to find the meaning of unknown words.

1. An *astronomer* is like a *geographer* except that _____

_____.

2. An *asterisk* is like a *question mark* because _____

_____.

3. An *aster* is like a *zinnia* because _____

_____.

4. *Binoculars* are like a *telescope* except that _____

_____.

5. *Mars* is like *Jupiter* except that _____

_____.

6. *Dusk* is like *dawn* because _____

_____.

7. *Sunshine* is like *moonlight* but _____

_____.

8. A *space shuttle* is like an *airplane* except that _____

_____.

9. *Stars* are like a *galaxy* except that _____

_____.

10. An *astronaut* is like an *explorer* because _____

_____.

Word Skills

Related Words

Words can be related in several ways. They may have the same suffix or prefix, the same root word, or similar meanings.

Circle the letter of the word that is not related to the others in each list. Then identify the category or relationship of the other words.

1. A astronaut
   B astrodome
   C ashtray
   D astronomer

_____

2. A astronomy
   B geology
   C story
   D chemistry

_____

3. A nautical
   B naughty
   C astronautics
   D aeronautics

_____

4. A astronomical
   B gigantic
   C enormous
   D size

_____

5. A rotation
   B rotten
   C rotating
   D rotary

_____

6. A aster
   B asterisk
   C astern
   D asteroid

_____

7. A vertical
   B horizontal
   C diagonal
   D astral

_____

8. A gas
   B gases
   C gash
   D gaseous

_____

Word Skills

Name _____ Date _____

Writing

Being a cosmonaut or astronaut can mean having exciting adventures. It can also mean facing the unknown. Did you ever think about being an astronaut? Would you like to be among the people who may live on a space station someday?

Write a paragraph explaining your feelings about being an astronaut or another kind of space traveler. Support your ideas by explaining why you would or would not like to go into space. Use some vocabulary words from this unit in your writing.

_____

_____

_____

_____

_____

_____

_____

_____

_____

Vocabulary in Context G4, SV 9780547625775

Writing

Climbing Mount Everest

Read the passage. Think about the meanings of the boldfaced words. Then go back to the passage. Underline the words or sentences that give you a clue to the meaning of each boldfaced word.

Edmund Hillary and Tenzing Norgay push their way through the snow. They look like visitors from another planet. They wear heavy suits, hoods, and goggles. They are tied together by a 12-foot rope. The date is May 29, 1953. The two men are **ascending** Mount Everest. It is the highest mountain in the world. They hope to reach its peak today.

Mount Everest is part of the Himalaya mountain range north of India. It rises $5\frac{1}{2}$ miles above sea level. Near the top of the mountain, the air is thin, and breathing is hard. Temperatures drop far below freezing. The wind is fierce. Mount Everest is a **treacherous** mountain.

Before Hillary and Norgay, seven climbing teams had tried to reach the top of Mount Everest. All of them had failed. Sixteen men had died trying to reach the **mountaintop**.

Hillary, from New Zealand, and Norgay, from Nepal, climb **uphill** slowly. They creep along at about 250 feet an hour. The last 1,100 feet are the worst. They move inch by inch along a dangerous **crest**. Part of it crumbles under their feet. The air is so thin that they must breathe through **oxygen masks**.

The final 500-foot climb to the top is very icy. With **heroic** effort, the two men push on. As they go, they cut steps in the snow. At 11:30 A.M., they reach the top. It is a **breathtaking** view! Most people could not even imagine this sight. The two men celebrate their **arrival** by shaking hands. Below them lie the ridges and peaks of the Himalayas. Edmund Hillary and Tenzing Norgay have made history. It has been an **incredible** day.

68

Name _____ Date _____

Context Clues

Read each sentence. Choose a word from the box that means the same as the underlined part of each sentence. Write the word on the line.

incredible	arrival	crest	breathtaking	treacherous
heroic	oxygen masks	ascending	mountaintop	uphill

1. It takes <u>extremely brave</u> people to try to climb Mount Everest.

    _____

2. Such a climb is <u>very dangerous.</u> _____

3. They are climbing <u>up the slope of a hill.</u> _____

4. Up that high, they breathe through <u>equipment that supplies the gas that</u>

    <u>all living things need.</u> _____

5. The climbers keep on <u>going up</u> anyway. _____

6. They must reach the <u>mountain's peak.</u> _____

7. The climb can offer sights that are so beautiful they are <u>hard to believe.</u>

    _____

8. Climbers know they are near the end of the climb when they reach <u>the top</u>

    <u>part</u> of the mountain. _____

9. Their <u>reaching of the journey's end</u> at the top means they are at the highest

    tip of the world. _____

10. It is a <u>thrilling and exciting</u> view from the top of Mount Everest.

    _____

Vocabulary in Context G4, SV 9780547625775

Name _____ Date _____

Synonyms

Synonyms are words that have the same or almost the same meaning.
Match the words from the box with their synonyms listed below. Write each
word on the line.

mountaintop   heroic   treacherous   incredible

1. peak _____

2. unbelievable _____

3. dangerous _____

4. fearless _____

Understanding Multiple-Meaning Words

The words in the box have more than one meaning. Look for clues in
each sentence to tell which meaning is being used. Write the letter of the
meaning next to the correct sentence.

crest	arrival	uphill
a. the top part	**a.** the reaching of the journey's end	**a.** toward a higher place
b. feathers on the head of a bird	**b.** person who arrives	**b.** difficult

_____ **1.** A jungle bird will often have a crest.

_____ **2.** They were riding in on the crest of the wave.

_____ **3.** The plane's arrival has been announced.

_____ **4.** She is a new arrival from another country.

_____ **5.** The trail is all uphill.

_____ **6.** It will be an uphill fight to win the race.

www.harcourtschoolsupply.com
© HMH Supplemental Publishers Inc. All rights reserved.

70

Vocabulary in Context G4, SV 9780547625775

Name _____ Date _____

Hidden Message Puzzle

Write a word from the box next to each clue. To find the message, copy the numbered letters in the matching numbered boxes at the bottom of the page. Then you will know where all mountain climbers want to go.

treacherous	incredible	crest	heroic	oxygen masks
breathtaking	ascending	uphill	arrival	mountaintop

1. going up ☐☐☐☐☐☐☐☐

2. thrilling ☐☐☐☐☐☐☐☐☐☐☐☐

3. brave and bold ☐☐☐☐☐☐
                          4

4. the top part ☐☐☐☐☐
                      2

5. peak of a mountain ☐☐☐☐☐☐☐☐☐☐☐☐
                            1

6. a climber's direction ☐☐☐☐☐☐
                                      3

7. very dangerous ☐☐☐☐☐☐☐☐☐☐☐
                        8

8. used for breathing ☐☐☐☐☐ ☐☐☐☐☐
                            6

9. the coming to a place ☐☐☐☐☐☐☐
                              7

10. impossible to believe ☐☐☐☐☐☐☐☐☐☐
                                              5

ANSWER: ☐☐ ☐☐☐ ☐☐☐ !
            1 2   3 4 5   6 7 8

Vocabulary in Context G4, SV 9780547625775

Vocabulary in Context

Analogies

Each pair of words in an analogy is related in the same way. Write the words from the box to complete the following analogies.

breathtaking	crest	heroic	mountaintop	oxygen mask

1. An _____ is to a *mountain climber* as a *snorkel* is to a *diver*.

2. _____ is to *hero* as *painting* is to *painter*.

3. A *forehead* is to a *face* as a _____ is to a *mountain*.

4. *Roof* is to *rooftop* as *mountain* is to _____.

5. *Victory* is to *success* as _____ is to *thrilling*.

Word Groups

Read each pair of words. Think about how they are alike. Write the word from the box that best completes each group.

arrival	ascending	incredible	treacherous	uphill

1. unbelievable, unimaginable, _____

2. incline, slope, _____

3. landing, homecoming, _____

4. dangerous, difficult, _____

5. climbing, rising, _____

Name _____   Date _____

Standardized Test Practice

Read the phrase. Look for the word or words that have the same or almost the same meaning as the boldfaced word. Circle the letter for the correct answer.

TIP

Always read all the answer choices. Many choices may make sense. But only one answer choice has the same or almost the same meaning as the boldfaced word.

1. **treacherous** slope
   A safe   C dangerous
   B pretty   D thrilling

2. reach the **mountaintop**
   A peak   C trees
   B bottom   D fossil

3. climbing **uphill**
   A downward   C faster
   B better   D higher

4. wave's **crest**
   A water   C inside
   B top   D middle

5. **incredible** view
   A intelligent   C sad
   B unbelievable   D bad

6. **ascending** the hill
   A going up   C asking
   B going to   D buying

7. **heroic** effort
   A weak   C little
   B heavy   D brave

8. **arrival** time
   A leaving   C wanting
   B coming   D waiting

9. use **oxygen masks**
   A breathing equipment
   B costumes
   C pencils
   D cups

10. **breathtaking** moment
    A long   C breathing
    B short   D thrilling

Vocabulary in

Classify/Categorize

The words in the left column are all adjectives with similar meanings. Check the appropriate boxes to show how each word may be used. Then add some descriptive words of your own and check the boxes as before.

	Describes Language	Describes an Image	Describes a Person
vivid			
colorful			
descriptive			
emphatic			
radiant			
vibrant			
picturesque			
vivacious			

Word Skills

Words in Context

Think about the meaning of the underlined word. Then answer each question or complete each sentence.

1. A picturesque description would give readers or listeners a(n) _____

   _____.

2. The painting showed a radiant sunset behind the mountains. Describe what

   might make it seem *radiant*. _____

   _____

3. Which of the following words might describe an emphatic speech?

   assertive _____   soothing _____   demanding _____

   timid _____   uncertain _____   powerful _____

4. Write five colorful words to describe a parade.

   _____

   _____

5. Write five descriptive words to tell about a tree.

   _____

   _____

6. Name three or more animals, plants, or things that have vibrant colors.

   _____

   _____

7. Would you like to have a vivacious friend? Explain your reasons.

   _____

   _____

Word Skills

Word Lines

Arrange each group of words in a word line. Explain how you decided to arrange them. The first one has been done for you.

1. fast, quick, rapid, speedy, swift

quick, fast, speedy, swift, rapid _____

Each word expresses something a degree faster than the one before. _____

2. vivid, lifelike, descriptive, picturesque

_____

_____

3. brilliant, bright, radiant, colorful, vibrant

_____

_____

4. blast, boom, bang, roar, thunder

_____

_____

5. bit, crumb, dot, drop, grain

_____

_____

6. glad, happy, joyful, merry, cheerful

_____

_____

Word Skills

Writing

It takes bravery to climb a mountain. It also takes bravery to do many everyday jobs, like being a firefighter or a police officer.

On the lines below, describe a brave person. The person may be a child or an adult. Explain what the person does that makes him or her brave. Use some vocabulary words in your writing.

My idea of a brave person is _____

_____

_____

_____

_____

_____

_____

_____

_____

_____

_____

_____

_____

_____

Writing

A "Peak" Experience

Read the passage. Think about the meanings of the boldfaced words. Then go back to the passage. Underline the words or sentences that give you a clue to the meaning of each boldfaced word.

A climber might be a **beginner**. She might be an expert. Either way, there is a school that will help this young person **achieve** her outdoor goals. Outward Bound offers training for many outdoor adventures, including mountain climbing. Young people might have bodies that are in really good shape, or they might not. Whether or not they have great **physical** abilities, they can learn to climb mountains.

Mountain-climbing students, in small groups, take a course that can last about three weeks. The students learn to read maps. They learn safety rules to help them **avoid** careless accidents. They pay close attention to the directions. They **concentrate** on each thing they need to learn. For example, they spend time learning the proper use of their **gear**, the equipment they need for a climb.

The students look up to their Outward Bound teachers. Each teacher is an **inspiration** to the young people. The teachers make the young people want to meet difficult challenges. They guide the students through climbing skills. They help students learn how to make choices. And they help them learn to work together.

The group works together to plan a mountain-climbing trip. When the climb is finished, the students have done something important for themselves. Everyone respects what the group has **accomplished**. Each member earns and **deserves** the praise and cheers of the teachers and other students.

Most people want to prove themselves. They have a **desire** to succeed. Outward Bound helps many young people do just that. Outward Bound teachers believe that a person who climbs a mountain can reach other peaks in life, too.

Context Clues

Meanings for the vocabulary words are given below. Go back to the passage and read each sentence that has a vocabulary word. If you still cannot tell the meaning, look for clues in the sentences that come before and after the one with the vocabulary word. Write each word from the box in front of its meaning.

concentrate	gear	achieve	avoid	accomplished
desire	inspiration	deserves	beginner	physical

1. _____ : having to do with the body

2. _____ : someone just starting to learn something

3. _____ : to keep away from

4. _____ : equipment used for a particular purpose

5. _____ : to pay very close attention

6. _____ : a longing; a strong wish

7. _____ : a person that other people look up to

8. _____ : carried out; done

9. _____ : has a right to; is worthy of

10. _____ : to succeed in reaching a goal

Challenge Yourself

1. Name two pieces of <u>gear</u> you would take on a fishing trip.

_____

2. Name two activities in which you are a <u>beginner</u>.

_____

Vocabulary in Context

Understanding Multiple-Meaning Words

The words in the box have more than one meaning. Look for clues in each sentence to tell which meaning is being used. Write the letter of the meaning next to the correct sentence.

gear	concentrate	physical
a. equipment	**a.** pay close attention	**a.** relating to the body
b. machine part	**b.** to bring close together in one place	**b.** a medical checkup

_____ **1.** The airplane pilot put down the landing gear.

_____ **2.** Pack the camping gear in the trunk of the car.

_____ **3.** Sue must concentrate on finishing her work.

_____ **4.** The workers will all concentrate in the dining room.

_____ **5.** The doctor will give her a complete physical.

_____ **6.** Swimming is good physical exercise.

Rewriting Sentences

Rewrite each sentence using one of the vocabulary words from the box.

avoid	desire	deserves

1. My brother is worthy of a medal for putting up with me!

_____

2. My dad said that we should keep away from poison ivy.

_____

3. To be a champion, you need the strong wish to win.

Antonyms

Remember that antonyms are words that have opposite meanings. Match the words in the box with their antonyms listed below. Write each word on the line.

| beginner | physical | accomplished | avoid |

1. mental _____

2. failed _____

3. approach _____

4. expert _____

Word Suggestion

Some words have almost the same meaning, but one fits in a sentence better. Choose the word from each pair that best completes the sentence. Write it on the line.

1. Everyone on our team has a _____ to win the race. (wish, desire)

2. Yuko is just a _____, but she is already very good. (beginner, starter)

3. I try to _____ being late to work. (escape, avoid)

4. Juan _____ a great task with his science project. (accomplished, succeeded)

5. If you try hard, you will _____ your goals. (do, achieve)

6. The band certainly _____ our praise for the way they played "The Star-Spangled Banner." (deserves, earns)

Unit 8
Vocabulary in Context G4, SV 9780547625775

Vocabulary in Context

Idioms

An idiom is a saying that has a particular meaning that is different from the meaning of each word by itself. The sentences below contain idioms. Draw a line to match each idiom with its meaning.

1. Avoid the ant beds like the plague.

2. The traffic threw our travel plans out of gear.

3. The winner had beginner's luck.

4. During the game, football players get physical.

5. The student keeps her nose to the grindstone.

A. concentrates without distraction

B. surprisingly good luck

C. upset the smooth running of something

D. stay far away from something you don't like

E. push or tackle another person

Base Words

Base words are words without any endings or other word parts added to them. For each word below, write its base word next to it on the line.

1. accomplished _____

2. desirable _____

3. achievement _____

4. inspiration _____

5. deserving _____

Standardized Test Practice

Read the phrase. Look for the word or words that have the same or almost the same meaning as the boldfaced word. Circle the letter for the correct answer.

TIP

This test will show how well you understand the meaning of the words. Think about the meaning of the boldfaced word before you choose your answer.

1. **concentrate** on work
   A rest your head
   B set your mind
   C set your clock
   D turn around

2. **achieve** a goal
   A set   C fail
   B reach   D forget

3. camping **gear**
   A trails   C equipment
   B days   D jokes

4. **physical** shape
   A mental   C imaginary
   B bodily   D wild

5. just a **beginner**
   A new learner   C manager
   B expert   D diver

6. **deserves** praise
   A needs   C wants
   B gives   D earns

7. **accomplished** much
   A did   C played
   B cried   D spent

8. **inspiration** to many
   A source of laughter
   B source of light
   C source of encouragement
   D source of trouble

9. **avoid** problems
   A rush toward
   B tell about
   C do
   D keep away from

10. a strong **desire**
    A wish   C rope
    B spice   D smell

Compare and Contrast

In the left column are names that tell about a person's level of experience or skill. Along the top are several features that may or may not apply to each label. Fill in each block as follows:

+ yes   - no   +/- maybe

Next, add two features of your own that apply to a few of the labels. Fill in each block as before.

	Paid	In Training	Proficient	Experienced	Related to Sports	Related to Hobbies		
amateur								
starter								
dabbler								
fledgling								
novice								
professional								
rookie								
trainee								
expert								
veteran								

Word Skills

Euphemisms

A **euphemism** is a word used instead of another word that may have an unpleasant connotation. Using a euphemism makes something sound nicer than it may really be.

In each pair below, the second sentence restates the first, using a euphemism. Complete each by replacing the underlined word(s) with a word from the box. The first has been done for you.

starter	antique	fledgling	novice

1. You say: The skateboard is <u>old</u> and <u>run-down</u>.

   I reply: No, it's an _____*antique*_____.

2. You say: You're just a _____ photographer.

   I reply: No. I'm an <u>amateur</u>, but I do have experience.

3. You say: You've never done this before and <u>don't know what you're doing</u>.

   I reply: I'm a _____.

4. You say: A _____ like Aiden isn't good enough for our team.

   I reply: He's a <u>rookie</u>. I think you should give him a chance.

Now try this. One sentence is given to you. Write a second sentence using a euphemism for the underlined word or phrase. You may replace it with a word or a phrase. The first has been done for you.

5. You say: I'm going to get drenched in that <u>downpour</u>!

   I reply: *Oh, that's just a little drizzle*_____.

6. You say: The paint on that sign has <u>practically disappeared</u>. I can't even read it.

   I reply: _____.

Word Skills

Using Antonyms

Choose antonym pairs from the box that match the pairs of definitions.
Write them on the lines.

professional	rookie	dabbler	trainer
amateur	expert	trainee	veteran

1. paid _____

   unpaid _____

2. enjoys something but doesn't take it seriously _____

   studies carefully and has a lot of knowledge about something

   _____

3. has spent many years in this job _____

   this is the first year in this job _____

4. is learning how to do a job _____

   is teaching someone how to do a job _____

Colloquialisms

A **colloquialism** is a way of saying something informally. For example, *buck* is a colloquialism for *dollar*.

Match the colloquialism in the box to the underlined word in each sentence. Write it on the line.

pro	R&R	rookie

1. The police captain assigned an experienced officer to work with the <u>recruit</u>.

   _____

2. Teresa hopes to be a <u>professional</u> golfer one day. _____

3. Ed went to the beach for some <u>rest and relaxation</u>. _____

Word Skills

Writing

The Outward Bound students who climb mountains achieve their goal. You could say that they have fulfilled a desire. What is something that you desire to do with your life?

On the lines below, tell about a goal that you would like to achieve. Why is the goal important to you? What can you do to help you fulfill your desire? Use some vocabulary words in your writing.

_____

_____

_____

_____

_____

_____

_____

_____

_____

_____

_____

Writing

Land of the Midnight Sun

Read the passage. Think about the meanings of the boldfaced words. Then go back to the passage. Underline the words or sentences that give you a clue to the meaning of each boldfaced word.

In most parts of the world, people depend on two **daily** events. They expect a **sunrise** every morning. They also expect a **sunset** every evening. People who live in the Arctic Circle do not depend on these daily events. At the icy northern tip of the world, dawn and **nightfall** do not come every day.

The Arctic Circle is near the North Pole. There, from March until September, the sun never drops below the **horizon**. Instead, it stays in the sky all night and all day. It shines with its usual **brightness**. That is why this area is known as "the land of the midnight sun."

This happens because of the **location** of the sun and Earth. Earth travels around the sun once each year. As Earth moves, sunlight hits different parts of it at different angles. Earth also spins. It makes one turn each day. This causes day and night in most parts of the world.

At the North Pole it is different. Earth's spinning does not always make the sun disappear from view. Instead, the sun stays overhead for six months. During that time, it is always daylight!

Not everyone would like to live around the North Pole. People would miss **twilight**. Twilight is the time of day when the sun has set but before the sky gets completely dark. People also would miss seeing **moonlit** nights.

However, the people in "the land of the midnight sun" are not always without moonlight. They have moonlight during the other six months. Then it is dark all day and all night. During these months people spend most of their time indoors. They play games, study, and work to while away the hours of darkness.

Context Clues

Meanings for the vocabulary words are given below. Go back to the passage and read each sentence that has a vocabulary word. If you still cannot tell the meaning, look for clues in the sentences that come before and after the one with the vocabulary word. Write each word from the box in front of its meaning.

brightness	twilight	horizon	location	nightfall
sunset	daily	moonlit	sunrise	Arctic

1. _____ : the region around the North Pole

2. _____ : the line where Earth and the sky meet

3. _____ : the time when the sun goes down; sundown

4. _____ : the time when the sun comes up in the morning; dawn

5. _____ : the time of day between sundown and complete darkness; dusk

6. _____ : happening every day

7. _____ : the coming of darkness at the end of the day

8. _____ : lighted by the moon

9. _____ : the place where someone or something is located

10. _____ : the quality of being bright

Compound Words

Remember that a compound word is made up of two or more words. Join one word from Column A with one from Column B to make four compound words. Write the new words.

Column A	Column B	
moon	set	1. _____
night	rise	2. _____
sun	fall	3. _____
sun	lit	4. _____

Cloze Paragraphs

Use the words in the box to complete the paragraphs. Reread the paragraphs to make sure they make sense

Arctic	location	brightness
daily	twilight	horizon

Eskimos are people who live in the cold lands of the

(1) _____. The (2) _____ of the Eskimos' land

is very far north. So, for part of the year, the sun's (3) _____

lights the sky. Then (4) _____ activities like fishing and hunting

can be done all day and all night.

Later the sun sinks below the (5) _____. The Eskimos

watch the (6) _____ begin. They know darkness and winter

will follow.

Word Puzzle

Write a word from the box next to each clue. Then write the words formed by the letters in the squares. You will have the answer to the riddle.

daily	brightness	Arctic	nightfall	horizon
sunset	twilight	moonlit	sunrise	locations

1. dim light before dark ☐ __ __ __ __ __ __

2. when darkness comes __ __ __ ☐ __ __ __ __ __

3. quality of being bright __ __ __ __ __ __ __ __ ☐ __ __ __

4. also called sundown ☐ __ __ __ __ __

5. lighted by the moon __ __ ☐ __ __ __ __

6. line where Earth and sky meet __ __ __ __ __ __ ☐

7. very cold region that is home to Eskimos and polar bears __ ☐ __ __ __ __

8. happening every day __ __ ☐ __ __

9. positions __ __ __ __ __ __ __ ☐ __

10. happening in the morning __ __ __ __ __ __ ☐

RIDDLE:
Why did the mother enjoy waking her son?

ANSWER:
She liked to see _____ _____ _____!

Vocabulary in Context

Rewriting Sentences

Rewrite each sentence using one of the vocabulary words from the box.

brightness	daily	horizon	sunrise	Arctic

1. The cowboy watched the horse ride off toward the line where Earth meets the sky.

_____

2. I read at least ten pages of a book every day.

_____

3. The ocean near the North Pole is the smallest of the five oceans.

_____

4. When I was camping, I woke every day as the sun came up.

_____

5. The lamp's quality of being bright hurt my eyes.

_____

Synonyms

Remember that synonyms are words that have the same or almost the same meaning. Cross out the word in each line that is not a synonym.

1. twilight   dusk   shade   sunset

2. place   location   find   area

3. nightfall   brightness   darkness   sundown

4. serious   moonlit   shining   bright

Vocabulary in Context G4, SV 9780547625775

Vocabulary in Context

Standardized Test Practice

Read each sentence. Pick the word that best completes the sentence. Circle the letter for the correct word.

TIP
Before you choose an answer, try reading the sentence with each answer choice. This will help you choose an answer that makes sense.

1. I eat an apple every day. It is my ____ treat.

  A vegetable   **C** daily

  B Saturday   **D** Arctic

2. It was between sundown and complete darkness. It was ____.

  A black   **C** sunrise

  B twilight   **D** morning

3. The day begins at dawn. Dawn is also called ____.

  A sunrise   **C** night

  B sunset   **D** afternoon

4. The sky is full of color as the sun goes down. It is ____.

  A sunrise   **C** morning

  B sunset   **D** noon

5. Reindeer live around the North Pole. They live in the ____.

  A jungle   **C** Arctic

  B twilight   **D** river

6. The night sky is bright. It is a ____ sky.

  A dark   **C** distant

  B sunrise   **D** moonlit

7. It is dark after sundown. ____ follows sundown.

  A Afternoon   **C** Nightfall

  B Morning   **D** Sunrise

8. The sky seems to meet the land. They meet at the ____.

  A horizon   **C** ocean

  B station   **D** twilight

9. The sun hurts my eyes today. Its ____ is blinding.

  A darkness   **C** distance

  B size   **D** brightness

10. We do not know where the store is. We forgot its ____.

  A owner   **C** brightness

  B location   **D** business

Vocabulary in Context

    Vocabulary in Context G4, SV 9780547625775

Name _____   Date _____

Classify/Categorize

Answer the following question with a word from the box.

temperate	tropical	alpine	arid
subterranean	habitat	Antarctic	aquatic

1. Which word is a label for all the others? _____

Use a word from the box to name the type of habitat in which you would find the following plants and animals. Add another inhabitant to the group.

2. coral, fish, eels, seaweed _____

_____

3. monkeys, parrots, alligators, vines _____

_____

4. desert tortoises, cactuses, rattlesnakes _____

_____

5. moles, earthworms, ants _____

_____

6. penguins, whales, seabirds _____

_____

7. grizzly bears, deer, maple trees _____

_____

8. mountain goats, pine trees, eagles _____

_____

Vocabulary in Context G4, SV 9780547625775

Word Skills

Analogies

Remember that analogies are made up of two pairs of words. Each pair is related in the same way.

Complete the analogies below. The first one is done for you.

1. *Desert* is to *habitat* as _____*oak*_____ is to *tree.*

2. *Freezing* is to *Arctic* as _____ is to *temperate.*

3. *Fawn* is to _____ as *pup* is to *wolf.*

4. *Burrow* is to *woodchuck* as *den* is to _____.

5. *Arid* is to *desert* as _____ is to *rain forest.*

6. *Jeep* is to *driving* as _____ is to *picture-taking.*

7. *Antarctic* is to *tropical* as *east* is to _____.

8. *Yes* is to *no* as *question* is to _____.

9. *Daily* is to *week* as _____ is to *year.*

10. *Alpine* is to _____ as *coastal* is to *beach.*

11. *Mole* is to *subterranean* as _____ is to *aquatic.*

12. *Nightfall* is to *sunset* as *dawn* is to _____.

Unit 9
Vocabulary in Context G4, SV 9780547625775

Word Skills

Name _____ Date _____

Word Families

Read the following groups of words. Look for the root or base word in the word family. Write the root or base word.

1. habitat, habitation, inhabit _____

2. humanist, inhuman, humanitarian _____

3. location, locality, locating _____

4. tropical, tropics _____

5. brighter, brightness, brighten _____

6. aquarium, aquamarine _____

7. temperate, temperature, temper _____

8. nonsense, sensitive, senseless _____

9. autobiography, autograph, automatic _____

10. terrain, subterranean, terrestrial _____

Dictionary Skills

Find the word *alpine* in a dictionary and answer the questions.

1. What are the guide words for the page?

_____

2. Does the word *alpine* come before or after the word *alpinist*?

_____

3. Is the word *alpine* a noun, a verb, or an adjective?

_____

4. How many syllables are there in *alpine*?

_____

5. What is one meaning of the word *alpine*?

_____

Vocabulary in Context G4, SV 9780547625775

Writing

Imagine that you and your family took a summer trip to "the land of the midnight sun." Write a postcard to a friend. Tell about the sights you have seen. Use the passage on page 88 for ideas. Include some facts you learned in the lesson.

On the lines below, write your postcard. Use some vocabulary words from this unit in your writing.

_____
(Date)

Dear _____,

_____

_____

_____

_____

_____

_____

_____

_____

Your friend,

_____

Writing

Tejano Music, a Hot Mix

Read the passage. Think about the meanings of the boldfaced words. Then go back to the passage. Underline the words or sentences that give you a clue to the meaning of each boldfaced word.

Music is coming from the stage. A band is beginning to **rehearse**, or practice, a song. Is it rock and roll? Is it country music? Is it hip-hop? Is it jazz? The answer to all these questions is yes! The hot sound called Tejano is a mix of all of these kinds of music. It echoes in **auditoriums** where the music is performed in many cities and towns.

Tejano music represents a mix of cultures, too. You can hear a cheerful polka beat in some of the songs. Polka music came to Texas with the German people more than 100 years ago. Tejano music uses everything! The words in Tejano songs can be in Spanish or English. They can also be a mix of the two.

The word Tejano means "Texan." But it has come to mean more. One meaning is the special kind of music. Music lovers are loud in their praise of Tejano music. They have great interest in it. All this **enthusiasm** for the music is very strong near the border of the United States and Mexico. But the beat has become **internationally** known beyond these two countries. A Tejano group that has recorded an **album** of songs can quickly become famous. Their CD of songs may be enjoyed by millions of people.

Tejano music has **appeal** for young and old alike. Adults like it. Many young people in their teens are fans. These **teenagers** may buy large pictures of their favorite singers. They look at these **posters** and dress like the Tejano stars.

The crowds at Tejano events never sit still. Chances are you will see **mobs** of people dancing when you hear the happy beat of Tejano. You will also hear long and loud clapping at the end of each song. This **applause** is for the singer, for the dancers, and for Tejano music.

Vocabulary in Context G4, SV 9780547625775

Name _____ Date _____

Context Clues

Read each sentence. Look for clues to help you complete each sentence with a word from the box. Write the word on the line.

teenagers	enthusiasm	album	applause	posters
rehearse	mobs	internationally	appeal	auditoriums

1. Many _____, often beginning at age thirteen, are big fans of Tejano music.

2. They show a lot of _____ for the hot, exciting mix of Tejano songs.

3. A Tejano group that records an _____ can be known all over the world.

4. Teens like to hang _____ that have the pictures of their favorite Tejano stars on them.

5. It is not unusual to read about _____ of fans going to a Tejano concert.

6. Most concerts are held in _____, large rooms with many seats and a stage.

7. Tejano musicians must _____ often so they can put on a good show.

8. Part of the _____ of Tejano music is that it is a mix of other kinds of music.

9. The Tejano sound has become _____ known by people of all ages in many countries.

10. At a concert, it seems that the _____, or clapping, never seems to stop!

Name _____   Date _____

Synonyms and Antonyms

Remember that **synonyms** are words that have the same or almost the same meaning. **Antonyms** are words that have opposite meanings.

Each word below is paired with a boldfaced vocabulary word. If the two words are synonyms, put a check (✓) under that heading. If the two words are antonyms, put a (✓) under that heading.

	Synonyms	Antonyms
1. **applause** – clapping	✓	____
2. **internationally** – locally	____	____
3. **enthusiasm** – energy	____	____
4. **teenagers** – babies	____	____
5. **posters** – pictures	____	____
6. **appeal** – disgust	____	____

Word Suggestion

Some words have almost the same meaning, but one fits in a sentence better. Choose the word from each pair that best completes the sentence. Write it on the line.

1. Fans filled with _____ for Tejano music live all over the world. (interest, enthusiasm)

2. The musicians will want to _____ the music before the concert. (rehearse, train)

3. There are three large _____ of my favorite singer covering the wall in my room. (signs, posters)

4. There were _____ of people at the concert last night. (mobs, herds)

Analogies

Remember that an analogy shows how two words go together in the same way as two other words. Write the words from the box to complete the following analogies.

mobs	album	auditoriums	applause

1. *Whistling* is to *mouth* as _____ is to *hands*.

2. *Swarms* is to *bugs* as _____ is to *people*.

3. *Book* is to *chapter* as _____ is to *song*.

4. *Theaters* is to *movies* as _____ is to *concerts*.

Dictionary Skills

Remember that **guide words** are the two words at the top of each dictionary page. They show the first and last entries on that page. All the word entries in between are in alphabetical order.

Look at the pairs of guide words. On the lines below each pair, write the words from the box that would appear on the same dictionary page. Be sure to put them in alphabetical order.

posters	internationally	applause	appeal
teenagers	auditoriums	album	mobs

active/awkward   hardy/useful

1. _____   5. _____

2. _____   6. _____

3. _____   7. _____

4. _____   8. _____

Name _____ Date _____

Yes or No?

Read each question. For a "yes" answer, write the word <u>yes</u> on the line. For a "no" answer, write a sentence that gives the correct meaning of the underlined word. Use the Glossary if you need help.

1. Can a <u>mob</u> be only one person?

_____

2. Is <u>applause</u> made with mouths?

_____

3. If you flew from Nashville, TN, to Phoenix, AZ, did you fly <u>internationally</u>?

_____

4. If it is time to <u>rehearse</u> with your dance partner, would you be in a swimming pool?

_____

5. If you were sitting in an <u>auditorium</u>, would you see a stage?

_____

Idea Completion

Complete the following sentences. Use the word in parentheses in your sentence.

1. I heard _____. (album)

2. I see _____. (posters)

3. On Joseph's birthday, _____. (teenagers)

4. The movie _____. (appeal)

5. I feel _____. (enthusiasm)

Vocabulary in Context G4, SV 9780547625775

Vocabulary in Context

Standardized Test Practice

Read each sentence. Pick the word that best completes the sentence. Circle the letter for the correct word.

TIP
Some tests put letters before the answer choices. Be sure to find the letter of the answer you think is correct and then circle it.

1. You **rehearse** before a _____.
   A concert   C greenhouse
   B botanist   D satellite

2. **Teenagers** are also _____.
   A plants   C houses
   B students   D schools

3. You may place **posters** on a _____.
   A jacket   C wall
   B nest   D dish

4. **Mobs** of Tejano fans can be _____.
   A melted   C noisy
   B adopted   D invisible

5. When an **album** is played, you hear _____.
   A music   C clicking
   B nothing   D buzzing

6. One sign of **enthusiasm** is _____.
   A cheers   C tears
   B yawns   D anger

7. **Auditoriums** are used for _____.
   A accidents   C cooking
   B parking   D performances

8. The **appeal** of a concert is _____.
   A good food   C sound sleep
   B live music   D good sailing

9. If you are known **internationally**, you are known all over the _____.
   A school   C state
   B country   D world

10. **Applause** is often _____.
   A sung   C refusing
   B transparent D loud

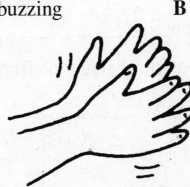

Rhyming Words

Turn the sentence and phrases below into rhymes by writing a word from the box on the line. The first one is done for you.

relaxation	repose	recreation	pleasure
pastime	leisure	diversion	amusement

1. Take a rest from sneezing.

   Repose _____ your nose.

2. There is no way to tell how much I enjoy soccer!

   You cannot <u>measure</u> my _____.

3. An activity that is only done during July and August

   is a <u>summertime</u> _____.

4. A place set aside for those who need to unwind from a hard day is a

   _____ <u>station</u>.

5. Someone who likes to work all the time and does not want to be disturbed

   has an <u>aversion</u> to _____.

6. The ballpark closed down, and the team had to find somewhere else to play.

   This was a case of _____ <u>relocation</u>.

7. I felt trapped inside all day by the heavy rains. My puppy thought it was a
   lot of fun having me at home all day.

   My <u>imprisonment</u> was my puppy's _____.

8. These piano lessons have taken all my free time from me.

   I would call that a <u>seizure</u> of my _____!

Name _____ Date _____

Using Synonyms

The words in the box are all related to recreation. Sort them into the diagram below according to their meaning.

amusement	pastime	pleasure	recreation
diversion	leisure	repose	relaxation

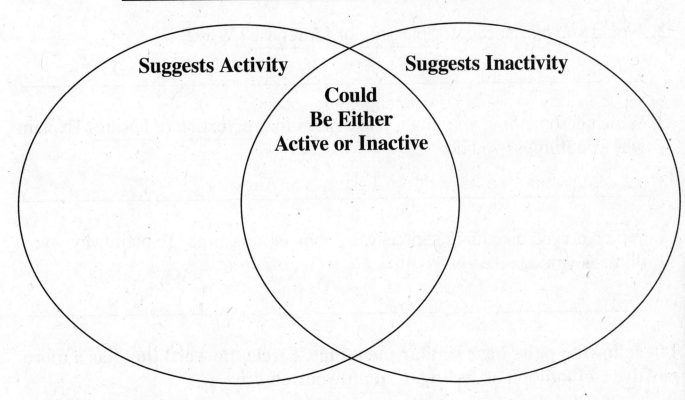

Suggests Activity   Suggests Inactivity

Could
Be Either
Active or Inactive

Now make a list of pastimes, or kinds of recreation, that are active and a list of pastimes that are not active.

Active Pastimes   Inactive Pastimes

_____   _____

_____   _____

_____   _____

_____   _____

_____   _____

Word Skills

Vocabulary in Context G4, SV 9780547625775

Name _____ Date _____

Connotation/Denotation

Think about the meanings of the underlined words. Answer the questions with complete sentences.

1. Would you prefer to do something for <u>amusement</u> or <u>relaxation</u>? Why?

_____

2. Would you play soccer for <u>pleasure</u> or for <u>repose</u>? Why?

_____

3. Which is something you might make plans for, <u>recreation</u> or <u>leisure</u>? Explain why you think as you do.

_____

4. Which do you take more seriously, a <u>hobby</u> or a <u>pastime</u>? Explain why you think as you do.

_____

The following pairs have similar meanings. Circle the word that has a more positive connotation or feeling. Explain your choice.

5. energetic   aggressive

_____

6. irritable   excitable

_____

7. uncivilized rugged

_____

8. forgetful   negligent

_____

Vocabulary in Context G4, SV 9780547625775

Word Skills

Writing

Tejano music is one kind of music that people like to listen to. Some other kinds of music that people like are classical, rock, rap, and country. What kind of music do you like to listen to?

On the lines below, tell about your favorite kind of music. Tell why you like it and what some of your favorite songs are. Use some vocabulary words from this unit in your writing.

_____

_____

_____

_____

_____

_____

_____

_____

_____

_____

Writing

Vocabulary in Context G4, SV 9780547625775

Glossary

A

accomplished	*verb*	did; carried out (page 78)
achieve	*verb*	to reach a goal (page 78)
active	*adjective*	working; continuing to act (page 18)
album	*noun*	a collection of recorded songs (page 98)
alpine	*adjective*	of, like, or located in mountains (page 94)
amateur	*noun*	a person who performs an activity for enjoyment rather than for money (page 84)
ambiance	*noun*	a surrounding atmosphere (page 34)
amusement	*noun*	the condition of being entertained; enjoyment (page 104)
anatomy	*noun*	the scientific study of the physical structure of the human body (page 54)
Antarctic	*noun*	of or having to do with the region of the South Pole (page 95)
antique	*noun*	something made long ago (page 85)
appeal	*noun*	charm; attractiveness (page 98)
applause	*noun*	clapping to show approval (page 98)
aquatic	*adjective*	living or growing in or on water (page 94)
arch	*noun*	a curved shape (page 28)
Arctic	*noun*	the area around the North Pole (page 90)
arid	*adjective*	without enough rainfall to grow things; dry (page 94)
arrival	*noun*	the time of coming to a place; the end of a journey (page 68)
artistic	*adjective*	done with good design and skill (page 8)
ascending	*verb*	climbing (page 68)
aster	*noun*	a plant with flowers like daisies (page 64)
asterisk	*noun*	a mark shaped like a star (*) used to show a note is provided (page 64)
asteroid	*noun*	any of thousands of tiny planets orbiting the sun between Mars and Jupiter (page 64)
astral	*adjective*	of or relating to the stars (page 64)

Vocabulary in Context G4, SV 9780547625775

astrodome	*noun*	a transparent dome on the top of an aircraft (page 64)
astronautics	*noun*	the science of flight in space (page 64)
astronomer	*noun*	a person who studies stars, planets, and other space objects (page 64)
atmosphere	*noun*	the air surrounding Earth (page 34)
auctioneer	*noun*	a person who conducts an auction (a public sale) (page 14)
auditoriums	*noun*	large rooms where people watch plays and concerts (page 98)
avoid	*verb*	to keep away from (page 78)

B

beginner	*noun*	a person who does something for the first time (page 78)
breathtaking	*adjective*	wonderful; splendid (page 68)
brightness	*noun*	the amount of light (page 88)

C

camels	*noun*	large desert animals that have one or two humps on their backs (page 38)
champion	*noun*	the winner of a contest; the person who comes in first (page 38)
climate	*noun*	the kind of weather a place has over a period of time (page 34)
coaxing	*verb*	urging; speaking softly to persuade (page 38)
colorful	*adjective*	full of bright colors (page 74)
competition	*noun*	contest; race (page 38)
competitor	*noun*	a person who competes in a contest (page 44)
composition	*noun*	the parts that make up something (page 54)
concentrate	*verb*	to pay close attention to; work carefully (page 78)
conflict	*noun*	struggle, fight, or battle (page 44)
conquer	*verb*	to win; to gain control of (page 58)
contender	*noun*	a person who has entered a competition (page 44)
cosmonaut	*noun*	a Russian who travels in space; see astronaut (page 58)

Vocabulary in Context G4, SV 9780547625775

crest	*noun*	the top part of a mountain (page 68)

D

dabbler	*noun*	someone who does something, but not very seriously (page 84)
daily	*adjective*	happening every day (page 88)
data	*noun*	facts; information (page 58)
delay	*noun*	a wait until a later time (page 58)
descriptive	*adjective*	telling what a person or thing is like (page 74)
deserves	*verb*	has rights to (page 78)
desire	*noun*	a strong wish; longing (page 78)
dismount	*verb*	to get down or off (page 38)
display	*noun*	a show (page 28)
diversion	*noun*	an amusement, game, or pastime done for relaxation or distraction (page 104)

E

emphatic	*adjective*	done or spoken with forceful speech (page 74)
engineer	*noun*	a person who is trained in the skill of putting scientific knowledge to practical use, as in the construction of roads, bridges, and machinery (page 14)
enthusiasm	*noun*	great interest and energy (page 98)
entries	*noun*	people who take part in a contest (page 38)
erupts	*verb*	throws out melted rock (page 18)
expert	*noun*	a person who has great knowledge of a skill or area (page 84)

F

fledgling	*noun*	a young, inexperienced person; beginner (page 84)
flee	*verb*	to run away (page 18)
focus	*noun*	to aim a light beam in a particular direction (page 8)
form	*noun*	the way in which someone does something (page 54)
frame	*noun*	a basic inner structure that gives support and shape to the thing built around it (page 54)

framework	*noun*	the basic inner structure around which a thing is built (page 54)
function	*noun*	job; usual work (page 48)
furnace	*noun*	a box that holds a very hot fire (page 18)

G

gear	*noun*	equipment (page 78)
geographer	*noun*	a person who studies the features of Earth's surface (page 24)
geologist	*noun*	a scientist who studies the history and structure of Earth (page 24)
glands	*noun*	parts of the body that take out materials from the blood for another use in the body (page 48)
gravity	*noun*	the pull of stars, planets, and moons on objects near them (page 24)

H

habitat	*noun*	the place where an animal or plant naturally lives or grows (page 94)
healthy	*adjective*	well; free from sickness (page 48)
heroic	*adjective*	very great or brave; far beyond the ordinary (page 68)
horizon	*noun*	where Earth and sky meet (page 88)

I

impress	*verb*	to have a strong effect on the feelings; amaze (page 8)
incredible	*adjective*	hard to believe (page 68)
inspiration	*noun*	a person who is looked up to and who makes others want to do difficult things (page 78)
insulate	*verb*	to keep from becoming too hot or too cold (page 48)
internationally	*adverb*	between or among nations (page 98)
invisible	*adjective*	not able to be seen (page 48)

Vocabulary in Context G4, SV 9780547625775

J

jeweler   *noun*   a person who sells, repairs, or makes jewelry (page 14)

L

launch   *verb*   to send into space (page 58)

lava   *noun*   the melted rock that flows from a volcano (page 18)

leisure   *noun*   time free from work, study, or other duties (page 104)

lifetime   *noun*   the time a person is alive (page 48)

location   *noun*   place where something is (page 88)

lunges   *verb*   moves forward suddenly (page 38)

M

magma   *noun*   the hot, partly liquid mass of rock within Earth (page 24)

marvel   *verb*   to be filled with wonder; to be amazed (page 8)

mature   *adjective*   grown-up; full-grown (page 48)

meet   *noun*   an assembly or gathering, as for a sports event (page 46)

mobs   *noun*   large crowds (page 98)

moisture   *noun*   wetness; dampness (page 28)

mold   *noun*   a type of fungus found on damp or decaying surfaces (page 54)

molten   *adjective*   melted; turned into a liquid by heat (page 18)

moonlit   *adjective*   lighted by the moon (page 88)

mountaineer   *noun*   a mountain climber (page 14)

mountaintop   *noun*   the top of a mountain (page 68)

N

nations   *noun*   countries; groups of people having the same government (page 58)

nerves   *noun*   body parts that carry signals between the brain and spine to parts like the eyes and muscles (page 48)

Vocabulary in Context G4, SV 9780547625775

nightfall	*noun*	dusk; the time when night comes (page 88)
normal	*adjective*	usual; expected (page 48)
novice	*noun*	a beginner or inexperienced person (page 84)

O

observe	*verb*	to see; to notice (page 28)
operators	*noun*	people who control machines (page 8)
opponent	*noun*	a person you are competing against in a contest (page 44)
orbited	*verb*	traveled around in a circle (page 58)
outruns	*verb*	runs faster than others (page 38)
overflows	*verb*	fills up and runs over (page 18)
oxygen	*noun*	a colorless, tasteless, odorless gas (page 34)
oxygen masks	*noun*	devices that give air to mountain climbers, pilots, and others at high altitudes (page 68)
ozone	*noun*	an unstable form of oxygen that has a sharp odor (page 34)

P

pastime	*noun*	something that makes time pass pleasantly, as a sport or hobby (page 104)
petroleum	*noun*	a dark, thick, oily liquid found in Earth and used to make fuels (page 24)
photographer	*noun*	a person who takes pictures with a camera (page 14)
physical	*adjective*	having to do with the body (page 78)
physician	*noun*	a doctor of medicine (page 8)
picturesque	*adjective*	having the kind of beauty suitable for a painted picture (page 74)
pioneer	*noun*	someone who leads the way, as in developing a new field (page 14)
pleasure	*noun*	a feeling of enjoyment, delight, or satisfaction (page 104)
posters	*noun*	large printed pieces of paper that can be put up on a wall (page 98)
produce	*verb*	to make; to give forth (page 8)

Vocabulary in Context G4, SV 9780547625775

professional	*noun*	someone working for money in a field often entered by amateurs (page 84)

Q
qualify	*verb*	to show that you are fit for something (page 38)

R
radiant	*adjective*	very bright and shining; brilliant (page 74)
raindrop	*noun*	a drop of rain (page 28)
rainstorm	*noun*	a storm that has much rain (page 28)
realistic	*adjective*	looking like real people or things; lifelike (page 8)
recreation	*noun*	an enjoyable activity or other form of amusement, relaxation, or play (page 104)
reflects	*verb*	sends back (page 28)
refuge	*noun*	a place that is safe from danger (page 18)
rehearse	*verb*	to practice over and over (page 98)
relaxation	*noun*	the act of resting from work or exercise (page 104)
repose	*verb*	to rest or sleep (page 104)
rival	*noun*	a person who tries to equal or outdo another; competitor (page 44)
rookie	*noun*	a beginner or novice, as in a professional sport (page 84)

S
satellite	*noun*	an object made by people that is sent into space by rocket (page 58)
scrape	*verb*	to scratch; to rub in a rough way (page 48)
sediment	*noun*	matter that settles to the bottom of a liquid (page 24)
seismograph	*noun*	an instrument that records the strength and duration of earthquakes (page 24)
senator	*noun*	a member of a governing body known as the senate (page 14)
skeleton	*noun*	the internal framework of bones that supports the body (page 54)
slopes	*noun*	the sides of mountains (page 18)

smog	*noun*	a blend of smoke and fog (page 34)
spacecraft	*noun*	rocket; a machine that travels in space (page 58)
spectacle	*noun*	something to look at; an amazing sight (page 38)
spectacular	*adjective*	wonderful to see (page 28)
spellbound	*adjective*	so interested that one cannot speak or move (page 8)
starter	*noun*	someone who starts something or is involved at the beginning of an activity, as in a race (page 84)
structure	*noun*	what something is made of (page 54)
subterranean	*adjective*	located or happening under Earth (page 95)
sunrise	*noun*	the appearance of the sun in the morning; the beginning of the day (page 88)
sunset	*noun*	the disappearance of the sun in the evening; the beginning of night (page 88)
surroundings	*noun*	the things or conditions around a person or place; environment (page 34)

T

teenagers	*noun*	people from 13 through 19 years old (page 98)
temperate	*adjective*	moderate in temperature (page 95)
tournament	*noun*	a series of matches in a sport or game involving many players or teams (page 44)
trainee	*noun*	a person who is being taught how to do something, as in a job (page 84)
transforms	*verb*	changes greatly (page 8)
treacherous	*adjective*	dangerous (page 68)
triumphant	*adjective*	successful (page 58)
tropical	*adjective*	of, having to do with, or located in the hot and humid region known as the tropics (page 95)
twilight	*noun*	the time between sunset and complete darkness (page 88)

U

uphill	*adverb*	up the side of a mountain or hill (page 68)

Glossary
Vocabulary in Context G4, SV 9780547625775

V

vapor   *noun*   moisture in the form of water droplets floating in the air as mist, fog, or steam (page 34)

veteran   *noun*   a person who has long experience in a particular field (page 84)

vibrant   *adjective*   full of energy; vigorous (page 74)

victor   *noun*   the winner, as in a contest or competition (page 44)

visible   *adjective*   able to be seen (page 28)

vivacious   *adjective*   full of life and spirit; lively (page 74)

vivid   *adjective*   clear and strong; bright; brilliant (pages 28 and 74)

volcanic   *adjective*   of, produced by, or thrown up from a volcano (page 24)

volunteer   *noun*   a person who offers to help or to work without pay (page 14)

W

warnings   *noun*   signs of possible danger (page 18)

Vocabulary in Context G4, SV 9780547625775

Answer Key

Page 9
1. produce
2. physician
3. artistic
4. realistic
5. focus
6. transforms
7. marvel
8. spellbound
9. operators
10. impress

Page 10
Rewriting Sentences
1. You should see a physician about that cut on your knee.
2. In a fairy tale, the kiss from a princess transforms a frog into a prince.
3. Our town has a factory that uses iron to produce steel.

Understanding Multiple-Meaning Words
1. a
2. b
3. b
4. a
5. a
6. b

Page 11
Analogies
1. marvel
2. produce
3. artistic
4. impress

Dictionary Skills
1. artistic: done with good design and skill
2. focus: to aim a light beam in a particular direction
3. impress: to have a strong effect on the feelings; amaze
4. operators: people who control machines
5. physician: a doctor of medicine

6. realistic: looking like real people or things; lifelike
7. spellbound: so interested that one cannot speak or move
8. transforms: changes greatly

Page 12
Answers will vary. Accept reasonable answers.

Page 13
1. A
2. B
3. C
4. D
5. A
6. C
7. B
8. C
9. D
10. C

Page 14
1. photographer; one who takes photographs
2. engineer; one who operates an engine
3. auctioneer; one who runs an auction
4. mountaineer; one who climbs mountains
5. senator; one who is elected to the Senate
6. jeweler; one who makes or repairs jewelry

Page 15
1. A
2. B
3. A
4. A
5. B
6. A
7. B
8. A

Page 16
1. C
2. A
3. C

Vocabulary in Context G4, SV 9780547625775

4. A
5. D
6. B

7–10. Accept reasonable answers.

Page 17
Answers will vary based on students' personal experiences.

Page 19
Context Clues
1. lava
2. warnings
3. furnace
4. molten
5. flee
6. active
7. slopes
8. refuge
9. overflows
10. erupts

Challenge Yourself
Answers will vary. Sample responses are provided.
1. hurricane, snowstorm
2. baseball, hiking

Page 20
Synonyms
1. warnings
2. overflows
3. erupts
4. refuge

Dictionary Skills
1. active
2. flee
3. furnace
4. lava
5. molten
6. slopes

Page 21
Across
2. flee
6. lava
7. active

8. slopes
9. refuge

Down
1. overflows
2. furnace
3. erupts
4. molten
5. warnings

Page 22
Word Groups
1. overflows
2. lava
3. flee
4. furnace
5. warnings
6. slopes

The Truth, Please
Answers will vary. Possible responses:
1. The hot molten rock covered up a tree.
2. As a volcano erupts, the mountain becomes loud and blows up.
3. A good place to take refuge from a tornado is a basement.
4. It is dangerous to build a city near the top of an active volcano.

Page 23
1. B
2. D
3. B
4. D
5. A
6. C
7. A
8. B
9. D
10. A

Page 24
Answers may vary. Accept reasonable answers for added words.
1. words related to rock formation
2. words related to volcanoes
3. occupations

4. words related to the solar system
5. things found in Earth
6. words with *geo-*
7. rocks and minerals
8. earthquake words

Page 25
Answers will vary. Sample responses are provided.
1. both are seasons.
2. gasoline is made from petroleum.
3. objects can escape the pull of gravity.
4. magma is molten rock.
5. both provide measurements.
6. a stalactite hangs from above.
7. the Rockies are in North America.
8. both are minerals.
9. iron rusts
10. both study objects found in the ground.

Page 26
1. geologist
2. melted
3. heroic
4. burned
5. volcanic
6. sedimentary
7. destroyed
8. geographer

Page 27
Answers will vary based on students' personal experiences.

Page 29
Context Clues
1. visible
2. rainstorm
3. display
4. raindrop
5. vivid
6. spectacular
7. arch
8. observe
9. reflects
10. moisture

Challenge Yourself
Answers will vary. Sample answers are provided.
1. bus, trees
2. balloon, sunset

Page 30
Word Groups
1. arch
2. reflects
3. observe
4. vivid
5. moisture
6. display

Cloze Paragraph
1. moisture
2. raindrop
3. rainstorm
4. display
5. visible
6. spectacular

Page 31
Compound Words
1. rainbow
2. raindrop
3. rainstorm
4. raincoat

Analogies
1. arch
2. reflects
3. display
4. visible
5. observe
6. spectacular
7. moisture
8. vivid

Page 32
Synonyms
1. boring
2. ignore
3. mistake
4. hidden
5. agreement

Vocabulary in Context G4, SV 9780547625775

6. roof

Glossary Skills
1. raindrop: a drop of rain
2. rainstorm: a storm that has much rain
3. reflects: sends back
4. visible: able to be seen
5. vivid: bright, brilliant

Page 33
1. C
2. D
3. B
4. C
5. B
6. A
7. C
8. D
9. D
10. A

Page 34
1. Science words: atmosphere, oxygen, ozone, vapor, smog, climate
2. Describes the area around you: atmosphere, ambiance, climate, surroundings
3. Weather words: smog, climate, vapor, ozone
4. Words with two syllables: vapor, climate, ozone
5. Accept reasonable answer.
6. Accept reasonable answer.

Page 35
1. A, B
2. B, A
3. B, A
4. A, B

Page 36
Categories
Categories and additional words will vary. Sample responses are provided.
1. D
   Category: synonyms for average weather
   Add: weather

2. B
   Category: gases
   Add: nitrogen
3. B
   Category: things you can't see or touch
   Add: air
4. C
   Category: synonyms
   Add: feeling
5. C
   Category: word family, related to sphere
   Add: hemisphere
6. D
   Category: things you see in the sky
   Add: stars

Page 37
Answers will vary based on students' personal experiences.

Page 39
1. camels
2. competition
3. qualify
4. entries
5. champion
6. outruns
7. coaxing
8. lunges
9. dismount
10. spectacle

Page 40
Base Words
1. camel
2. coax
3. mount
4. entry
5. lunge

Word Groups
1. outruns
2. competition
3. champion
4. spectacle
5. qualify

Vocabulary in Context G4, SV 9780547625775

6. lunges

Page 41
1. champion
2. entries
3. dismount
4. coaxed
5. lunges
6. competition
7. camel
8. qualify
9. outruns
10. spectacle

To what part of the word would you go to see the King's Camel Race?

The <u>Middle</u> <u>East</u>

Page 42
Synonyms
1. cross out *current*
2. cross out *sink*
3. cross out *normal*
4. cross out *rests*
5. cross out *disqualified*
6. cross out *worst*

Rewriting Sentences
1. At the end of the race, riders <u>dismount</u>.
2. Use <u>coaxing</u> to get the mule to walk.
3. I saw three <u>camels</u> at the zoo.
4. There are many <u>entries</u> in the science fair.

Page 43
1. B
2. C
3. A
4. D
5. B
6. B
7. D
8. A
9. C
10. D

Page 44
Possible answers:

1. sculptor
2. winner
3. artistic
4. contest
5. throne/crown
6. index
7. margins/lines
8. application
9. (any vegetable)
10. sportsmanship

Page 45
1. B; base word *compete*
2. D; base word *contend*
3. D; base word *oppose*
4. B; base word *rival*
5. D; base word *victor*
6. A; base word *tour*
7. B; word part *-ing*
8. D; word part *con-*

Page 46
Possible answers:

1. A; types of competitions
2. C; people taking part in a competition
3. C; games played with a net
4. B; parts of a baseball diamond
5. D; protective gear worn by baseball players

Page 47
Answers will vary based on students' personal experiences.

Page 49
Context Clues
1. lifetime
2. scrape
3. normal
4. nerves
5. function
6. glands
7. insulate
8. healthy
9. invisible
10. mature

Challenge Yourself

Answers will vary. Sample responses are provided.

1. eat well, bathe
2. gloves, scarf

Page 50
Synonyms

1. normal
2. function
3. invisible
4. healthy
5. mature
6. scrape

Writing Sentences

Answers will vary but should show an understanding of each word's meaning.

Page 51

Parts of the Body: glands, nerves; additional words will vary

How a Body Can Look: mature, normal, healthy; additional answers will vary

What a Body Can do: answers will vary

Page 52
Idea Completion

Answers will vary.

Word Groups

1. normal
2. mature
3. function
4. insulate
5. glands

Page 53

1. C
2. D
3. B
4. A
5. C
6. D
7. B
8. A
9. D
10. B

Page 54

1. B
2. B
3. A
4. A
5. B
6. A
7. B
8. B

Page 55

1. anatomy
2. drama
3. social studies
4. grammar
5. mathematics
6. physical education
7. architecture
8. science
9. Answers will vary.
10. Answers will vary.

Page 56

Answers will vary. Accept reasonable answers.

Page 57

Answers will vary based on students' personal experiences.

Page 59

1. nations
2. conquer
3. delay
4. satellite
5. triumphant
6. launch
7. data
8. orbited
9. spacecraft
10. cosmonaut

Page 60
Analogies

1. cosmonaut
2. delay
3. satellite

4. spacecraft

5. nation

Word Groups

1. nations

2. launch

3. orbit

4. data

5. triumphant

6. conquer

Page 61

Rewriting Sentences

1. The spacecraft sat on the launch pad, waiting for the countdown to begin.

2. There was a parade after the astronaut's triumphant return from space.

3. The pilot had to delay our flight to Miami.

4. I keep all that data stored on my laptop.

5. The satellite orbited Earth.

6. Heads of state of different nations will meet in Toronto.

The Truth, Please

Answers will vary. Suggested responses are provided.

1. Like the moon, a **satellite** orbits Earth.

2. If you **conquer** something, you triumph and win it.

Page 62

Descriptions

1. spacecraft

2. nations

3. cosmonaut

4. launch

5. satellite

Explore Word Meanings

Sentences will vary but should include the underlined word and one circled word.

1. circle *army, invader*

2. circle *football game, appointment, flight*

Page 63

1. A

2. C

3. B

4. C

5. B

6. D

7. B

8. C

9. D

10. A

Page 64

Possible answers are given:

1. someone who sails through the stars

2. the science of traveling in space

3. studies the stars

4. something that resembles a star

5. having to do with the stars

6. An astrodome might be a clear, rounded roof through which people might look at the stars.

7. a drawing of a plant with star-shaped or daisy-shaped flowers

Page 65

Answers will vary. Sample responses are provided.

1. an astronomer studies stars.

2. both are punctuation marks.

3. both are shaped like stars.

4. binoculars view objects from a closer distance.

5. Mars is smaller.

6. both involve the sun.

7. the sun provides sunshine, not the moon.

8. a space shuttle flies in space.

9. a galaxy is a group of stars.

10. both explore new places.

Page 66

1. C; same root word

2. C; sciences

3. B; same root word

4. D; similar meanings

5. B; same root word

6. C; same root word

7. D; directions

8. C; same root word

Page 67
Answers will vary based on students' personal experiences.

Page 69
1. heroic
2. treacherous
3. uphill
4. oxygen masks
5. ascending
6. mountaintop
7. incredible
8. crest
9. arrival
10. breathtaking

Page 70
Synonyms
1. mountaintop
2. incredible
3. treacherous
4. heroic

Understanding Multiple-Meaning Words
1. b
2. a
3. a
4. b
5. a
6. b

Page 71
1. ascending
2. breathtaking
3. heroic
4. crest
5. mountaintop
6. uphill
7. treacherous
8. oxygen masks
9. arrival
10. incredible
ANSWER: to the top

Page 72
Analogies
1. oxygen mask

2. Heroic
3. crest
4. mountaintop
5. breathtaking

Word Groups
1. incredible
2. uphill
3. arrival
4. treacherous
5. ascending

Page 73
1. C
2. A
3. D
4. B
5. B
6. A
7. D
8. B
9. A
10. D

Page 74
Describes Language: vivid, colorful, descriptive, emphatic

Describes an Image: vivid, colorful, radiant, vibrant, picturesque

Describes a Person: colorful, emphatic, radiant, vibrant, picturesque, vivacious

Additional words will vary. Accept reasonable answers.

Page 75
1. Possible answer: picture/image in their minds of the thing being described
2. Possible answer: There might be rays of light shining through openings in the clouds.
3. Check assertive, demanding, powerful
4. Possible answers: brilliant, shining, golden, scarlet, glittery
5. Possible answers: sturdy, shady, leafless, gnarled, ancient
6. Possible answers: a parrot, a kaleidoscope, a cardinal, a neon sign

Vocabulary in Context G4, SV 9780547625775

7. Possible answer: Yes, a vivacious person would be friendly and full of life and would be fun to be around.

Page 76
Answers will vary. Possible answers are given.

1. quick, fast, speedy, swift, rapid
   Each word expresses something a degree faster than the one before.

2. descriptive, picturesque, vivid, lifelike,
   Each word describes a more lifelike quality than the one before.

3. bright, colorful, vibrant, radiant, brilliant
   Each word describes something a shade brighter than the one before.

4. bang, boom, blast, thunder, roar
   Each word indicates a louder noise than the one before.

5. grain, dot, drop, crumb, bit
   Each word indicates something larger than the one before.

6. glad, cheerful, happy, merry, joyful
   Each word is happier than the one before.

Page 77
Answers will vary based on students' personal experiences.

Page 79
Context Clues
1. physical
2. beginner
3. avoid
4. gear
5. concentrate
6. desire
7. inspiration
8. accomplished
9. deserves
10. achieve

Challenge Yourself
Answers will vary. Suggested responses are provided.

1. fishing poles, net
2. playing chess, using a computer

Page 80
Understanding Multiple-Meaning Words
1. b
2. a
3. a
4. b
5. b
6. a

Rewriting Sentences
1. My brother deserves a medal for putting up with me!
2. My dad said that we should avoid poison ivy.
3. To be a champion, you need the desire to win.

Page 81
Antonyms
1. physical
2. accomplished
3. avoid
4. beginner

Word Suggestion
1. desire
2. beginner
3. avoid
4. accomplished
5. achieve
6. deserves

Page 82
Idioms
1. D
2. C
3. B
4. E
5. A

Base Words
1. accomplish
2. desire
3. achieve
4. inspire
5. deserve

Vocabulary in Context G4, SV 9780547625775

Page 83

1. B
2. B
3. C
4. B
5. A
6. D
7. A
8. C
9. D
10. A

Page 84

amateur	-	+/-	+/-	+/-	+	+		
starter	+/-	+	-	-	+	+		
dabbler	-	+/-	-	-	+	+		
fledgling	+/-	+	-	-	+	+		
novice	+/-	+	-	-	+	+		
professional	+	+/-	+/-	+/-	+/-	+/-		
rookie	+	+	-	-	+	+		
trainee	+/-	+	+/-	-	+	-		
expert	+/-	-	+	+	+	+		
veteran	+/-	-	+	+	+	+		

Additional answers will vary.

Page 85

1. antique
2. fledgling
3. starter
4. novice
5. Oh, that's just a little drizzle.
6. Possible answer: The paint does seem a little dull.

Page 86

Using Antonyms

1. professional, amateur
2. dabbler, expert
3. veteran, rookie
4. trainee, trainer

Colloquialisms

1. rookie
2. pro
3. R&R

Page 87

Answers will vary based on students' personal experiences.

Page 89

1. Arctic
2. horizon
3. sunset
4. sunrise
5. twilight
6. daily
7. nightfall
8. moonlit
9. location
10. brightness

Page 90

Compound Words

1. moonlit
2. nightfall
3. sunset or sunrise
4. sunrise or sunset

Cloze Paragraphs

1. Arctic
2. location
3. brightness
4. daily
5. horizon
6. twilight

Page 91

Answer to the riddle: the son rise

1. twilight
2. nightfall
3. brightness
4. sunset
5. moonlit
6. horizon
7. Arctic
8. daily
9. locations
10. sunrise

Page 92
Rewriting Sentences
1. The cowboy watched the horse ride off toward the horizon.
2. I read at least ten pages of a book daily.
3. The Arctic Ocean is the smallest of the five oceans.
4. When I was camping, I woke every day at sunrise.
5. The brightness of the lamp hurt my eyes.

Synonyms
1. shade
2. find
3. brightness
4. serious

Page 93
1. C
2. B
3. A
4. B
5. C
6. D
7. C
8. A
9. D
10. B

Page 94
1. habitat
2. aquatic; additional inhabitants will vary
3. tropical; additional inhabitants will vary
4. arid; additional inhabitants will vary
5. subterranean; additional inhabitants will vary
6. Antarctic; additional inhabitants will vary
7. temperate; additional inhabitants will vary
8. alpine; additional inhabitants will vary

Page 95
2. warm
3. deer
4. Possible answer: bear
5. humid/wet
6. camera
7. west

8. answer
9. monthly
10. mountains
11. Possible answer: fish
12. sunrise

Page 96
1. habit
2. human
3. locate
4. tropic
5. bright
6. aqua
7. temp
8. sense
9. auto
10. terra

Dictionary Skills
1. Answers will vary.
2. before
3. adjective
4. two
5. Answers will vary.

Page 97
Answers will vary based on students' personal experiences.

Page 99
1. teenagers
2. enthusiasm
3. album
4. posters
5. mobs
6. auditoriums
7. rehearse
8. appeal
9. internationally
10. applause

Page 100
Synonyms and Antonyms
1. synonyms
2. antonyms
3. synonyms
4. antonyms

5. synonyms

6. antonyms

Word Suggestion

1. enthusiasm

2. rehearse

3. posters

4. mobs

Page 101

Analogies

1. applause

2. mobs

3. album

4. auditoriums

Dictionary Skills

1. album

2. appeal

3. applause

4. auditoriums

5. internationally

6. mobs

7. posters

8. teenagers

Page 102

Yes or No?

1. A mob is a large crowd.

2. Applause is made by clapping hands.

3. To fly internationally, one would have to fly from one country to another.

4. You would rehearse in a studio where you could practice your dance moves.

5. Yes

Idea Completion

Answers will vary.

Page 103

1. A

2. B

3. C

4. C

5. A

6. A

7. D

8. B

9. D

10. D

Page 104

2. pleasure

3. pastime

4. relaxation

5. diversion

6. recreation

7. amusement

8. leisure

Page 105

Suggests Activity: recreation, amusement

Could Be Either Active or Inactive: pleasure, diversion, pastime

Suggests Inactivity: relaxation, repose, leisure

Active Pastimes: Possible answers: biking, playing soccer, swimming, playing basketball, running, playing an instrument

Inactive Pastimes: Possible answers: reading, playing board games, listening to music, watching TV, collecting stamps, talking on the phone

Page 106

1–4. Answers will vary. Accept reasonable answers.

5. energetic; accept a reasonable explanation

6. excitable; accept a reasonable explanation

7. rugged; accept a reasonable explanation

8. forgetful; accept a reasonable explanation

Page 107

Answers will vary based on students' personal experiences.

Vocabulary in Context G4, SV 9780547625775